MW00827773

Sasquatch / Bigfoot

The Search for North America's Incredible Creature

by Don Hunter
with René Dahinden

M&S

Canadian Cataloguing in Publication Data
Hunter, Don, 1937–
    Sasquatch / Bigfoot

Rev. ed.
Previously published under title: Sasquatch.
ISBN 0-7710-4298-1

1. Sasquatch.   I. Dahinden, René.   II. Title.

QL89.2.S2H86 1993   001.9'44   C93-093171-8

Printed and bound in Canada

McClelland & Stewart Inc.
The Canadian Publishers
481 University Avenue
Toronto, Ontario M5G 2E9

With thanks to the following for their invaluable assistance:

Don Abbott, British Columbia Provincial Museum, Victoria, B.C.; Dmitri Bayanov and Igor Bourtsev, Moscow; Dr. Dmitri Donskoy, U.S.S.R. Central Institute of Physical Culture, Moscow; Bob Gimlin, Yakima, Washington; Don Grieves, the Royal Free Hospital of Medicine, London, England; Prof. Grover Krantz, Washington State University, Pullman, Washington; Dr. John Napier, Birckbeck College, London University, England; Prof. Jack W. Ondrack, University of Alberta, Edmonton; the late Prof. Boris Porshnev, Science Academy of the U.S.S.R.; Dr. T.D. Stewart, Smithsonian Institution, Washington, D.C.; Mrs. Henedine Therrien, Richmond, B.C. Also to all those whose stories appear in these pages. DH

PROLOGUE

Just after midnight on Sunday, March 15, 1987, in the snow-bound oil-patch country near Dawson Creek in northeast British Columbia, a gang of seven men from an Alberta oil crew worked busily on a rig. The night was cloudless, and the moon, reflected off the snow, lit the cleared area around the worksite. The crew was involved in dangerous work, and an ambulance was on standby. The men were in a state of full-alert, ready for anything.

Well, almost anything.

One of the riggers was thirty-year-old Myles Jack. As he worked, a shadowy movement at the edge of some nearby bush caught his eye. He estimated the distance at between fifty and seventy-five yards.

Jack stopped work and stared out towards the spot. As he did, a creature he later described as "more like a man than an animal" stood suddenly upright from a kneeling position. Jack and others who subsequently saw it estimated that the creature stood between seven and eight feet and weighed between 350 and 400 pounds.

Jack called to his buddy Brian Mestdagh, busy moving a load of liquid carbon dioxide, and pointed out the "big hairy man." As Mestdagh turned, the creature, which he saw clearly, ran, still upright, off into the bush.

"It was a real mover," Jack said later. "It was really fluid in the way it moved." And he said the creature took "huge steps–twice the length of that of the average man." Measurements of the thing's footprints would support that. The hair-covered creature then circled the clearing around the oil rig, peering intermittently at the men as it did so, and twice crossed the unpaved access road that ran through the camp.

"It was like we were on his property and he was checking us out," Jack told reporters.

Four of the seven crew members got a good look at the creature, and all of them–experienced outdoorsmen and hunters–dismissed any chance of it being a bear. Some of them tried to track it, using flashlights to follow its footprints, but found it impossibly heavy-going between the trees in two feet of snow–where the creature had moved with ease and speed. Mestdagh said of the sighting afterwards: "I've never really had a feeling like that. It was like someone touched a live spark-plug wire to my back. It was really...just frightening, is all."

The men returned to Dawson Creek, and word of their experience spread. The story was greeted with predictable laughter and references to the rough-necks' legendary capacity for alcohol. But there had been no drinking on that job. And a hotel desk clerk, Agnes Smith, had taken particular note of their return to the hotel at about 3:00 a.m. The bar was closed when they arrived, and the men asked her if she could get them a bottle of whiskey. "They were white and they were shaking," she told reporters later, remarking that these were men who lived with danger every minute of their working lives. She said, "They said they had seen something they had never seen before, and I believed them." She also made sure they got their whiskey.

In the hotel at the same time was a reporter from the *Vancouver Province*, that city's morning paper. Ann Rees, a seasoned and respected journalist, was in Dawson Creek with photographer Les Bazso on another story, one which soon took a back seat. Agnes Smith told Rees about the crew's report, and the next day Rees and Bazso were out at the rig site at first light.

The creature's footprints were clearly visible in the powdery snow, two feet long and six feet apart. Rees also noticed V-shaped markings, which she felt could have been made by two knees touching the snow, and behind these, two indentations, which could have been formed by the toes of someone or something in a kneeling position.

She was convinced that whatever else the sighting was, it was no hoax. "I don't know what they saw, but they saw something," she recalls. "I don't see where they could have had the time to stage something like that." And while agreeing that a prankster could not be ruled out, she noted the improbability of someone running round in a gorilla suit at that time of night and year, in that latitude, in an area accessible only by four-wheel-drive vehicles.

In one of a number of press interviews the men subsequently gave, Myles Jack said, "I never imagined I'd see anything like that in my lifetime." And Brian Mestdagh added, "I don't care whether people believe me or not, I saw what I saw."

Ann Rees's story was front page in the next day's *Province*. She immediately followed that with an interview with a man generally regarded as one of the world's experts in the realm of sightings of the mysterious hair-covered creature.

His name is René Dahinden. The Dawson Creek incident is one of hundreds that he has examined in four decades of intense, relentless investigation. He counts it as one of the more impressive in his files. He has others that are considerably less impressive–a number of elaborate hoaxes, which we shall examine later in this book.

Before that, though, another remarkable story from René's files deserves to be considered. It took place seventeen years before the oil-patch event, and about 800 miles to the south.

In the middle of the afternoon of January 7, 1970, Bill Taylor, a works foreman with the British Columbia Department of Highways, drove north on Highway 99 between Squamish (pop. 6,121) and Pemberton (pop. 157) about sixty miles northwest along the coast from Vancouver. The day was sunny, clear and cold. There was frost on the ground and patches of snow lay on the rocky cliffs that meet the road on the east, and in crevices in the steep, rock-strewn bank that cuts down to the Cheakamus River, one thousand feet below on the west side. Taylor had met another department truck by arrangement, loaded some spare parts onto his three-quarter-ton pickup, and turned and headed back towards Pemberton.

As he rounded a sharp turn near the top of Cheakamus Canyon he saw, about two hundred feet ahead on the left shoulder of the road, what he at first took to be a bear. The creature appeared to step towards the highway, then it stumbled and fell on all fours, its back to Taylor who had stopped his truck to watch. He was now only eighty feet away.

What the highways foreman saw in the next half minute or so is imprinted in his mind and will stay there for as long as he lives.

The creature stood up, turned and glared at the watching man and, walking upright with arms swinging, crossed the forty-foot-wide highway in four or five quick strides, climbed a ten-foot bank, using its left hand once to gain purchase, and disappeared over the bank. In its right hand it carried a fish, the head and tail of which protruded from the closed fist on either side. There was no doubt in Bill Taylor's mind that what he had seen was not a bear.

But if not a bear, then what?

Consider his description of the creature:

"I first estimated its height at about seven feet and its weight at about three hundred pounds. Later I re-enacted the scene with a tall man and adjusted that to estimate the height at at least eight feet and the weight between seven hundred and eight hundred pounds–minimum. Its body was covered with reddish brown hair about three to four inches long. The forehead sloped to the rear and the head came to a point. The hair on its face was either much shorter or much lighter than that on its body because I could see very clearly an expression–of either anger or fear. The eyebrows were prominent, the nose was flat, and the eyes were like a human's. It measured about three feet across the shoulders and had a very prominent stomach. Generally, it was monkey-like with human eyes: it was simply a hairy, large creature that scared the daylights out of me."

The description in each of these stories is that of the creature known in British Columbia as Sasquatch, in California and the north-western United States as Bigfoot. Essentially it is considered–by those who accept its existence–to be a sub-human creature (the scientific terms will find their natural place later in this book) with an appearance and posture vaguely resembling those of man and with the habits and mentality of an animal. It is thought to be omnivorous, possessed of enormous strength, and to be generally non-aggressive to man, though apparently curious about him, as we shall see. It has been called the Abominable Snowman of North America and indeed much of the reference to it and the descriptions of it are paralleled by those linked to the Yeti of the Himalayas. But the data surrounding the Sasquatch–including scores of face-to-face confrontations–make the Yeti by comparison seem of little substance. Under a variety of names it is found in the culture of virtually all North American Indians, and in many of Central and South America. And many of them are in no doubt as to its existence today. For them it lives as surely as do the bears and the deer whose habitat it shares. It was an old man of the Salish people in British Columbia who said, when the Sasquatch began to command the news pages: "So the white man has finally got around to that, has he?"

What Bill Taylor saw on Highway 99 mirrors the object of scores of sightings that have been reported in British Columbia, Washington, Oregon, and northern California during the last hundred years or so. There have been variations in the descriptions of hair colour and length, of body bulk and height, but the average is the essence of Taylor's report: a hairy, brownish humanoid creature, upwards of eight feet tall and weighing up to one thousand pounds, walking upright and taking six-to-eight-foot strides. It communicates by way of a high-pitched whistling scream. It leaves footprints up to twenty-four inches long and eight inches wide. Many of the prints suggest a foot structure almost identical to the human foot, and they leave impressions several inches deep on surfaces where a heavy man makes scarcely a mark. It is these footprints (thousands of them) that the serious investigator today cites as firm evidence that the Sasquatch exists. They and the claims for them–and the claims against them–will be considered at length in this book.

For now, let's return to Bill Taylor. A married man with two children, a Highways Department foreman in the Pemberton area for four years at the time of the incident, obviously held as a responsible man by his employers, and considered a respected and reliable family man by his neighbours.

For him to see a Sasquatch, or whatever it was he saw, was to find himself, from one point of view, in an awkward spot. That's from the viewpoint that people who see Sasquatch in British Columbia–or anywhere else for that matter–are immediately suspect; fair game especially for the humorists of newspaper and radio: see a Sasquatch, and risk your reputation and credibility by talking about it. In fact it is the fear of being ridiculed, the constant Sasquatch hunter feels, that has served to limit the available body of knowledge. He believes there are hundreds more who have seen the creature, or its tracks, but who have chosen to stay silent rather than be mocked and have their integrity and good sense questioned–or, more likely, judged entirely missing.

Put yourself in the position: you're going home to tell your friends and family that you have just seen a hairy, eight-foot ape-man, weighing half a ton, crossing the road in half a dozen strides. The odds are good that before you arrive you'll have elected for silence.

Bill Taylor could have remained silent. He had nothing to gain by telling. He had no witness to support his story and little chance of finding anything at the site to prove it. But he apparently never considered the possibility, or the implications, of being ridiculed, or, if he did, he dismissed them. What he had seen, at close hand and in perfect visibility, he had seen; and he was troubled by it.

Hurrying the four miles to where a gang was working, Taylor grabbed another foreman and took him back to the spot. They found one rock where the thing had stepped and where the frost layer had been compressed and melted to a thin ice. The rest of the frozen ground in the area provided no trace of the creature. Taylor could have dropped the matter there, could have laughed it off with the other foreman, dismissing it as a bear. Instead, later that day, he entered the incident in his daily log book where it was read by his district superintendent. What this man's views were on the Sasquatch is not known, but he apparently knew his foreman well enough to take the story seriously. He persuaded the foreman–who was going to be content to make the official report his last mention of the incident–to talk to people who were known to have a particular interest in the Sasquatch. At this point René Dahinden entered the story. For him it was one more step in his intense pursuit of proof of the existence or–equally important to him–the non-existence of the Sasquatch.

Dahinden, a Swiss-born Canadian adventurer, has investigated with an exhaustive thoroughness countless stories of Sasquatch sightings, thousands of footprints–and not a few Sasquatch hunters themselves. He has badgered every branch of science in North America that could possibly relate to the existence of a hairy bipedal giant hominid, with little success. For the most part he has met with responses that ranged from vague expressions of "cautious interest" to the attitude of: "It can't exist, therefore it doesn't exist." (As we shall see later in this book, the latter attitude particularly has undergone some modifications in some minds in North America within the last two years. From outside of North America we'll see a prominent British scientist state categorically his belief that the Sasquatch does exist, and his intriguing arguments for that conclusion.) René has suffered hoaxers and publicity hounds, and outright fakers intent on making a quick dollar. It's certain that he has collected more data and scrutinized it more thoroughly than any of the other handful of persistent Sasquatch seekers.

He has never seen a Sasquatch; he is not easily persuaded by those who say they have seen one. While he is as objective and skeptical as a man could be in analysing physical "evidence" offered as proof of the Sasquatch's being, when it comes to stories of sighting, such as Bill Taylor's story, there is only that most subjective of all measures–human judgment–to depend on. He expresses doubt about many stories, rejects firmly many others. Of Bill Taylor he says: "My impression was of an honest man. I spoke to Highway Department workers who knew him and who had a high regard for him, and to many in the community who shared this regard. All of them said they had formerly rejected the possibility of Sasquatch existing. But, they said, if Bill Taylor saw it, then it's true."

Bill Taylor's story, like that of Myles Jack and his friends seventeen years later near Fort St. John, echoes a number of others that will be studied in the following pages as part of the whole Sasquatch saga: he either told the truth, told a lie, or made a mistake in identification. Given the conditions of that day, his nearness to the creature, and his experience as an outdoorsman, the third possibility can be erased. As with others involved in similar incidents, Taylor had no apparent motive for relating the incident other than his feeling that it must be reported. He sought no publicity; in the brief reports of the event Taylor's name was not used. He told no one, initially, other than his fellow foreman, his superintendent, and his own family–who were considerably upset by what he told them.

The incident raises the question that has been raised repeatedly in other similar incidents: why would this person, in his situation, say that he saw this creature, and so graphically describe it, if he didn't see it? And the only logical reply of course is that he–and the others–did see it, and that it does exist.

The Taylor story is part of the mountain of material collected by Dahinden that seems to point more and more to the evidence of the Sasquatch's existence. Yet Dahinden will not claim unconditionally that it *does* exist. His concern is to prove *whether* it exists. By the end of this book the information he has gathered will have been presented and the reader may draw his own conclusions.

Before plunging into the Sasquatch story, though, there are three statements worth considering. They capsulize Dahinden's approach and the attitudes of the opposing views of science to the Sasquatch question.

The first comes from T.D. Stewart, Anthropologist Emeritus at the Smithsonian Institution, Washington, D.C. I had written him with a question about some bones that were found in Minnesota and which some sources said might have been from the Neanderthal period. Had this been the case it might have caused some re-alignment in Sasquatch thinking among some authorities. Dr. Stewart indicated such was not the case, and he went one further:

"...the characterization of the Minnesota skeletal find as 'Neanderthaloid' is bosh, just as is Bigfoot."

As it happened, Dr. Stewart was quoting to me from a reply he had given to another questioner on the subject: Dr. John Napier, the source for our second statement. And as it happens, Dr. Napier was director of primate biology at the Smithsonian, and later held a similar position at Birkbeck College, University of London. Dr. Napier published (November, 1972) a book titled *Bigfoot.* In it he pursues the mystery of giant footprints in various parts of the world, including those left by Sasquatch. And he concludes:

"I am convinced the Sasquatch exists...."

The third statement comes from René Dahinden. He says:

"*Something* is making those goddamn footprints and I'm going to find out what it is."

CHAPTER 1

The earliest-known "recorded" references to the Sasquatch are found on the carved totem poles and masks of the coast Indians of British Columbia, particularly on those of the Kwakiutls. A main feature on the poles is a representation of the *Dsonoqua* (Cannibal Woman) with her son sitting on her lap and held close to her body, while one of the popular masks of their culture is a ferocious-looking and remarkably detailed face of the *Bukwas*, or Wild Man of the Woods. Each of the carvings, in its stylized way, suggests a creature that is considerably more human in appearance than it is animal.

The Kwakiutls believed the *Dsonoquas* to be people who lived, in houses, deep in the woods and mountains. They described them as being black, hairy, with deep-set eyes, and twice as big as a man. The female seems to have dominated the Kwakiutl stories and frequent reference is made to her large, pendulous breasts (a feature remarked on by a number of those involved in sightings in recent years).

Kidnapping and cannibalism by the *Dsonoqua* are common themes in the Kwakiutl stories, as they are in tales of the Sasquatch told by the Salish Indians of British Columbia's Fraser Valley and those of the western part of the state of Washington. And the creatures' intrinsic malevolence is perhaps further attested to in the legend which describes how a group of Indians was able to burn alive a family of the cannibals: the remaining ashes turned into mosquitoes, and such was the beginning of that source of torment.

With minor variations in behaviour and appearance, the creature under its many names plays a major role in western Indian lore from northern B.C. to California, and a somewhat lesser though similar role in native culture across the continent. Hairy giants, with human attributes of varying degree, are ubiquitous.

To the Indians there was nothing terribly mythical about the creature. It existed in their day-to-day world and it was not something to be messed about with.

Some native attitudes are recorded in the notes and diaries of the early explorers, such as this extract from *Noticias De Nutka* by Jose Mariano Mozino (published in Spanish in 1792, and translated by Iris Higbie Wilson. University of Washington Press, Seattle and London, 1970) :

> I do not know what to say about the matlox (Sasquatch), inhabitant of the mountainous districts, of whom all have an unbelievable fear. They imagine his body as very monstrous, all covered with stiff black bristles; a head similar to a human one but with much greater, sharper and stronger fangs than those of the bear; extremely long arms; and toes and fingers armed with long curved claws. His shouts alone (they say) force those who hear them to the ground, and any unfortunate body he slaps is broken into a thousand pieces.

When David Thompson crossed the Rockies near the present site of Jasper, Alberta, in the winter of 1811, he kept a daily journal. Years later this was incorporated into the publication of his "Narrative", in which he notes:

> (January 5) ...we are now entering the defiles of the Rocky Mountains by the Athabasca River ... strange to say, here is a strong belief that the haunt of the Mammoth is about this defile...I questioned several (Indians), none could positively say they had seen him, but their belief I found firm and not to be shaken. I remarked to them, that such an enormous heavy animal must leave indelible marks of his feet, and his feeding. This they all acknowledged, and that they had never seen any marks of him, and therefore could show

me none. All I could say did not shake their belief in his existence....

(January 7) Continuing our journey in the afternoon we came on the track of a large animal, the snow about six inches deep on the ice; I measured it; four large toes each of four inches in length to each a short claw; the ball of the foot sunk three inches lower than the toes, the hinder part of the foot did not mark well, the length fourteen inches, by eight inches in breadth, walking from north to south, and having passed about six hours. We were in no humour to follow him; the men and Indians would have it to be a young Mammoth and I held it to be the track of a large old grizzled bear; yet the shortness of the nails, the ball of the foot, and its great size was not that of a bear, otherwise that of a very large old bear, his claws worn away; this the Indians would not allow....

Thompson makes no suggestion that the tracks were made by a quadruped, and it has to be significant that the Indians rejected the bear theory. The dimensions given are considerably bigger than those normal for a grizzly (though they are not inconceivable for a particularly big bear), and the grizzly has five short toes, not four long ones. Exactly what the Indians meant by "Mammoth" is not detailed, but from the references I think we can reasonably speculate that it is our mystery creature.

Another explorer, the artist Paul Kane, also comments on the Indians' recognition of a strange creature, in his book, *The Wanderings of An Artist*, published in 1925. His entry for March 26, 1847, reads:

When we arrived at the mouth of the Kattlepoutal River, twenty-six miles from Vancouver (Washington), I stopped to make a sketch of the volcano, Mt. St. Helens, distant, I suppose, about thirty or forty miles. This mountain has never been visited by either whites or Indians; the latter assert that it is inhabited by a race of beings of a different species, who are cannibals, and whom they hold in great dread ... these superstitions are taken from the statement of a man who, they say, went into the mountain with another, and escaped the fate of his companion, who was eaten by the "skoo-cooms", or "evil genii." I offered a considerable bribe to any Indian who would accompany me in its exploration but could not find one hardy enough to venture there.

Kane's comments make no reference to the "skoo-cooms" being ape-like, but they are especially interesting in light of the events which occurred much later on Mt. St. Helens and which we deal with in this chapter and later ones.

Another story of a quite gruesome experience with a bipedal giant is related by Theodore Roosevelt in his book, *Wilderness Hunter,* and concerns events of about the mid-1800's. Roosevelt writes:

(The story) was told(to me) by a grizzled, weather-beaten old mountain hunter named Baumann, who was born and had spent all his life on the frontier. He must have believed what he said for he could hardly repress a shudder at certain points....

When the event occurred Baumann was still a young man and was trapping with a partner in the mountains dividing the forks of the Salmon River from the head of the Wisdom River. Not having had much luck, he and his partner decided to go up into a particularly wild and lonely pass through which ran a small stream said to contain many beaver. The pass had an evil reputation because the year before a solitary hunter who had wandered into it was slain, seemingly by a wild beast, the half-eaten remains being found afterwards by some mining prospectors who had passed his camp only the night before.

The memory of this event however weighed very

lightly with the two trappers, who were as adventurous and hardy as others of their kind ... they reached a little open glade where they concluded to camp, as signs of game were plenty.

The story describes the pair building a brush lean-to, and making a check of the stream and setting a few traps before returning to camp....

They were surprised to find that during their absence something, apparently a bear, had visited and had rummaged about among their things, scattering the contents of their packs, and ... destroying their lean-to. The footprints of the beast were quite plain but at first they paid no particular heed to them....

When Baumann's partner finally did check the prints his response was: "Baumann, that bear has been walking on two legs."

Roosevelt's story continues:

...Baumann laughed at this but his partner insisted that he was right, and upon again examining the tracks with a torch, they certainly did seem to be made by but two paws or feet. However it was too dark to make sure. After discussing whether the footprints could be possibly those of a human being, and coming to the conclusion that they could not be, the two men rolled up in their blankets and went to sleep....

At midnight Baumann was awakened by some noise and sat up in his blankets. As he did so his nostrils were struck by a strong wild-beast odour and he caught the loom of a great body in the darkness at the mouth of the lean-to. Grasping his rifle he fired at the vague, threatening shadow, but must have missed, for immediately afterwards he heard the smashing of the underwood as the thing, whatever it was, rushed off into the impenetrable blackness of the forest and night.

The pair sat up most of the night, and stayed close together the next day as they set more traps. They came back to camp as evening approached....

On nearing it they saw, hardly to their astonishment, that the lean-to had again been torn down. The visitor of the preceding day had returned and in wanton malice had tossed about their camp kit and bedding and destroyed the shanty. The ground was marked up by its tracks and on leaving the camp it had gone along the soft ea by the brook, where the footprints were as as if on snow, and, after a careful scrutiny the trail, it certainly did seem as if, whatever ng was, it had walked on but two legs.

Thn ... kept up a roaring fire throughout the nione or the other sitting on guard most of the e. About midnight the thing came down through the forest opposite ... and stayed there on the hillside for nearly an hour. They could hear the branches crackle as it moved about and several times it uttered a harsh, grating, long-drawn moan, a peculiarly sinister sound. Yet it did not venture near the fire.

The trappers decided it was time to leave and began preparations....

The whole morning they kept together, picking up trap after trap, each one empty. On first leaving camp they had the disagreeable sensation of being followed. In the dense spruce thickets they occasionally heard a branch snap after they had passed, and now and then there were slight rustling noises in the small pines to one side of them.

At noon they were back within a couple of miles of camp. In the high bright sunlight their fears seemed absurd to the two armed men, accustomed as they were through long years of lonely wandering in the wilderness to face every kind of danger from man, brute, or element. There were still three beaver traps to collect from a little pond ... Baumann volunteered to gather these and bring them in, while his companion went ahead to camp and made ready the packs.

By the time Baumann had finished his chores with the beaver traps, the sun was going down....

He came to the edge of the little glade where the camp lay, and shouted as he approached it, but got no answer. The camp fire had gone out, though the thin blue smoke was still curling upwards.

Near it lay the packs, wrapped and arranged. At first Baumann could see nobody; nor did he receive an answer to his call. Stepping forward he again shouted, and as he did so his eye fell on the body of his friend, stretched beside the trunk of a great fallen spruce. Rushing towards it the horrified trapper found that the body was still warm, but that the neck was broken, while there were four great fang marks in the throat.

The footprints of the unknown beast, printed deep in the soft soil, told the whole story.... It had not eaten the body, but apparently had romped and gambolled around it in uncouth and ferocious glee, occasionally rolling it over and over; and had then fled back into the soundless depths of the woods....

Baumann fled the area, pursued by grim and horrible imaginings of what kind of creature he had been up against.

The outstanding aspect of both Kane's and Baumann's stories is the element of violence, something which, with two exceptions that we shall deal with shortly, had played little part in the accounts of meetings with the creature in this century. Perhaps an explanation for this is that while man has extended his boundaries into the territories concerned, he has at the same time for the edification of all creatures, amply displayed his own boundless potential for destruction and slaughter. Any creature that has watched the performance of a modern-day Nimrod, armed to the eyebrows with enough explosive power to clear out a healthy part of any forest, surely would have sensed, if not reasoned, the wisdom of avoiding combat.

Reports of sightings of the Sasquatch during the last century were not limited to the Pacific Northwest. One which originated in the Memphis *Enquirer,* was subsequently printed in the New Orleans *Times Picayune* and the Galveston *Weekly Journal.* It gives a description of the appearance and behaviour of a creature that bears a close resemblance to our subject. The story tells of a "wild man" spotted by hunters in Greene County, Arkansas. The hunters saw a herd of cattle fleeing from something, then saw the cause of the cows' concern: "...an animal bearing the unmistakable likeness of humanity. He was of gigantic stature, the body being covered with hair and the head with long locks that fairly enveloped the neck and shoulders. The wild man, after looking at them deliberately for a short time, turned and ran away with great speed, leaping twelve to fourteen feet at a time. His footprints measured thirteen inches each."

The story added that the same creature had been reported by hunters for the past seventeen years and that "...a painter indeed saw him very recently but (and here's a familiar cry) withheld his information lest he should not be credited, until the account (of the hunters) placed the existence of the animal beyond cavil." No doubt the painter and the hunters would be surprised to know the extent of the objections to their wild man's existence that still exists today.

Similar stories to this are found in yellowing clippings from old newspapers in towns spotted the length and width of North and South America.

A familiar call from Sasquatch dissenters is: "Show me one and I'll believe it." Had one of them been in the small British Columbia railroad town of Yale in the Fraser Canyon during the year 1884, his call would have been answered. It was there that the only recorded instance of the capture of a Sasquatch took place. The incident was recorded in a telegraph dispatch which was printed in the Victoria (B.C.) *Colonist* on July 4th of that year. Under three banks of headlines: *"What is it? A strange creature captured above Yale. A British Columbia Gorilla,"* it reads as follows:

In the immediate vicinity of No. 4 tunnel, situated some twenty miles above this village (Yale), are bluffs of rock which have hitherto been insurmountable, but on Monday morning last were successfully scaled by Mr. Onderdon's employes (sic) on the regular train from Lytton. Assisted by Mr. Costerton, the British Columbia Express Company's messenger, and a number of men from Lytton and points east of that place who, after considerable trouble and perilous climbing, succeeded in capturing a creature which may truly be called half man and half beast. "Jacko," as the creature has been called by his capturers, is something of the gorilla type standing about four feet seven inches in height and weighing 127 pounds. He has long, black, strong hair and resembles a human being with one exception, his entire body, excepting his hands (or paws) and feet are covered with glossy hair about one inch long. His forearm is much longer than a man's forearm, and he possesses extraordinary strength, as he will take hold of a stick and break it by wrenching it or twisting it, which no man living could break in the same way. Since his capture he is very reticent, only occasionally uttering a noise which is half bark and half growl. He is, however, becoming daily more attached to his keeper, Mr. George Tilbury, of this place, who proposes shortly starting for London, England, to exhibit him. His favourite food so far is berries, and he drinks fresh milk with evident relish. By advice of Dr. Hannington raw meats have been withheld from Jacko, as the doctor thinks it would have a tendency to make him savage. The mode of capture was as follows: Ned Austin, the engineer, on coming in sight of the bluff at the eastern end of the No. 4 tunnel saw what he supposed to be a man lying asleep in close proximity to the track, and as quick as thought blew the signal to apply the brakes. The brakes were instantly applied, and in a few seconds the train was brought to a standstill. At this moment the supposed man sprang up and, uttering a sharp quick bark, began to climb the steep bluff. Conductor R.J. Craig and express messenger Costerton, followed by the baggageman and brakesmen, jumped from the train and knowing they were some twenty minutes ahead of time immediately gave chase. After five minutes of perilous climbing the then supposed demented Indian was corralled on a projecting shelf of rock where he could neither ascend nor descend. The query now was how to capture him alive, which was quickly decided by Mr. Craig, who crawled on his hands and knees until he was about forty feet above the creature. Taking a small piece of loose rock he let it fall and it had the desired effect of rendering poor Jacko incapable of resistance for a time at least. The bell rope was then brought up and Jacko was now lowered to terra firma. After firmly binding him and placing him in the baggage car, "off brakes" was sounded and the train started for Yale. At the station a large crowd who had heard of the capture by telephone from Spuzzum Flat were assembled, each one anxious to have the first look at the monstrosity, but they were disappointed, as Jacko had been taken off at the machine shops and placed in charge of his present keeper.

The question naturally arises, how came the creature where it was first seen by Mr. Austin. From bruises about its head and body, and apparent soreness since its capture, it is supposed that Jacko ventured too near the edge of the bluff, slipped, fell, and lay where found until the sound of the rushing train aroused him. Mr. Thos. White and Mr. Gouin, C.E., as well as Mr. Major, who kept a small store about half a mile west of the tunnel during the past two years, have mentioned having seen a curious creature at different points between Camps 13 and 17, but no attention was paid to their remarks as people came to the conclusion that they had seen either a bear or a stray Indian dog. Who can unravel the mystery that now surrounds Jacko? Does he belong to a species hitherto unknown in this part of the continent, or is he really what the train men first thought he was, a crazy Indian?

The newspaper account of Jacko has since been confirmed by an old man, August Castle, who was a child in the town at the time. He was not taken to see the creature but he remembers clearly that the events were as the newspaper reported them. The unfortunate thing about the Jacko story is that the captive's ultimate fate is not known. Washington State University anthropologist Grover Krantz who has done, and still is doing, considerable research into the Sasquatch phenomenon (Chapters 8 and 9), received information from a game guide named Chilco Choate at Clinton, B.C. Choate said his grandfather, who was a judge in Yale at the time, saw Jacko and that the creature, accompanied by Mr. Tilbury, was shipped east by rail in a cage, on the way to an English sideshow. Neither Tilbury nor Jacko was ever heard from again in Yale and it was presumed the creature had died in transit and had been disposed of. Choate's grandfather described Jacko as "an ape." Certainly from the description of the covering of glossy hair alone, the "crazy Indian" thesis seems improbable. The North American Indian is conceded to be of Mongolian derivation, a people of whom a particular characteristic is a sparsity of facial and body hair.

The next documented incident was reported in 1901, again in the Victoria *Colonist*. Mike King at that time was one of the best known timber cruisers (men who search out good, accessible stands of timber for the logging companies) in the province and was, according to the *Colonist,* "a fine type of man with an enviable reputation for reliability." He was working on Vancouver Island, near Campbell River, about one hundred miles northwest of Vancouver. Mr. King was working alone as his Indian packers had refused to accompany him into the woods at that place, because of their fear of what they called the "monkey men" of the forest. It was late in the afternoon when he saw the "man beast," bending over a pool of water, washing roots which it then placed in two neat piles. The creature finally either heard or saw King. It gave a startled cry and ran swiftly up a hillside, finally stopping at some distance and looking back at the man, who prudently kept his rifle trained on the thing. King described the creature as: "Covered with reddish brown hair, and his arms were peculiarly long and were used freely in climbing and in brush running; while the trail showed a distinct human foot, but with phenomenally long and spreading toes."

Three years later, on December 14, 1904, the *Colonist* reported that "four credible witnesses will attest that (the Sasquatch) is no myth or phantom of Indian imagination.

"A.R. Crump, J. Kincaid, T. Hutchins, and W. Buss, four sober-minded settlers of Qualicum (seventy miles south of Campbell River on the Island) are the new witnesses and there is not the slightest deviation or variation of detail in the stories they tell with an earnestness which defies ridicule."

The four were hunting in the interior of Vancouver Island when they saw what they described as a "living, breathing and intensely interesting modern Mowgli. The wild man was apparently young with long matted hair and a beard, and covered with a profusion of hair all over his body. He ran like a deer through the seemingly impenetrable undergrowth and pursuit was utterly impossible."

The *Colonist* placed great emphasis on the credibility of the witnesses. One wonders why the newspaper, apparently convinced by now of the Sasquatch's existence, never promoted a search for the creature. Perhaps it was "above" that sort of escapade; or perhaps it was still sufficiently English to believe in the Englishman's devout policy of minding one's own business. Whatever the case, the apparent credibility of those involved is all we have to go with.

A rather more dramatic event was reported in 1907 when the captain of the steamship *Capilano*, sailing up the B.C. coast, suddenly found himself being hailed by a canoe load of Indians, frantic to get away from their small community of Bishop's Cove. They had been scared away by a "monkey-like wild man who appears on the beach at night, who howls in an unearthly fashion between intervals of exertion at clam digging." There's an element of the ludicrous in this, if only in the image of the great creature howling as it pursues the somewhat prosaic pastime of digging clams. Nevertheless, the Indians did desert their village.

Unfortunately the records of the Victoria *Colonist* are not the stuff by which science is convinced, or even mildly persuaded. Of Jacko the knowledgeable ones say: "Probably an escaped circus ape"; despite there being no clue that any circus was within a thousand miles of the Fraser Canyon at the time. So the remarkable story of Jacko must simply be presented and weighed as part of the Sasquatch compendium.

Of the many incidents that have occurred this century, several have included reports of Sasquatches being shot at and hit. One of the earliest, and probably the most celebrated, was the affair that took place in a canyon on Mt. St. Helens–the same mountain mentioned by the explorer-artist Paul Kane–in July of 1924. Since the incident the place has been called Ape Canyon. The story was related to René Dahinden by Fred Beck in Kelso, Washington. Along with three other prospectors, he was in the area where they had worked for about six years, on and off, but which they would not work again after the events of one day and one night that July. Mr. Beck tells the story:

27

"We had been in and out of there for six years. We had seen big tracks around but we didn't bother much about them. This time we were doing some heavy blasting; maybe that attracted the things. Anyway, we started hearing a lot of strange whistling sounds from the surrounding ridges, and some heavy pounding, which we later considered must have been them beating their chests.

"It was just after sunrise, when we went to get water from a spring, that we saw the first one; we saw a big hairy face behind a tree. My father-in-law, Smith, loosed three shots at it from a .35 automatic Remington. We figured the thing had been hit in the head; the bullets creased the tree–it had to be hit in the head. My father-in-law said, 'Don't hurry, that thing won't go far.' We got to the tree, and there was nothing. And then we saw it running down a canyon about a quarter of a mile away. We fired two more shots but we couldn't tell if they hit or not.

"My father-in-law, who was a very well-known hunter and a crackshot, was scared they would come back at night. We went to bed that night–there were no windows in the cabin and it was made of logs that were between ten inches and two feet through–and soon afterwards there was a lot of bumping and banging on the roof. The chinking from one log was pushed through and it landed on Smith's legs. Then a hand came through, grabbed an axe that was leaning against the wall, and started to pull it through the opening. I turned the axe head, jamming it, and fired three shots up along the handle, and the axe came loose again.

"Next we heard the things running around outside like a bunch of horses, and then rocks were thrown on the roof and at the walls. Something tried to break the door down, but it held. We fired shots through the walls where we could hear the things. The noises went on to about three a.m.; we never saw anything because of there being no windows; just heard them.

"While the noise was going on my father-in-law sang to

them: 'If you leave us alone, we'll leave you alone; we'll go home first thing in the morning.' He was scared, and so were the rest of us.

"The next morning, being very careful, we went down to the mine tunnel; I was going in to fetch a rope out. I looked up and saw one of them with its back to me. I fired three shots and saw the fur fly (I was using a 30.30 Winchester), and the thing pitched forward and rolled down a steep canyon into the creek. We went down after it, but found nothing. We figured that either the water or some of its own tribe had carried it away.

"We didn't stay any longer; we went home. We went back once, some time later, and found the shack almost destroyed and sacks of tools and provisions destroyed and strewn all over the place. We took two Portland detectives with us when we went back. They found tracks nineteen inches long on the creek banks–the prints had only four toes; there was nothing where the little toe would have been. The detectives said we had probably seen bears."

Pretty strange bears, according to Beck's description of them: "About eight feet tall with wide shoulders tapering to small hips. They had deep chests and were covered in hair–but not terribly long hair. We estimated their weight at between eight hundred and one thousand pounds, and they walked like a man."

Earlier, we referred to there being two occasions in this century where the creatures had demonstrated a bent for violence. The Beck story was the first. The second did not occur until twenty-six years later, in 1950, but it also happened on Mt. St. Helens, near Ape Canyon, and so finds a place at this point in the saga. The circumstances make it one of the more unsettling events on record. We call it the case of the vanishing skier.

One balmy May Sunday, on the slopes near Ape Canyon, a well-known Seattle mountaineer named Jim Carter disappeared in circumstances that were, to say the least, mysterious. No trace of Carter, who was with a twenty-member climbing party, was ever found although teams of experienced mountain rescue units scoured the area for a week.

As the party came down the mountain Carter left them at the 8,000-foot level, near a landmark called Dog's Head. He said he would go ahead and photograph the others as they skied towards the timber line. That was the last time he was seen. The next morning a discarded film box was found at the spot where presumably he had loaded his camera.

Carter's ski tracks indicated he had raced down the mountain, as one searcher described it in a story in the Oregon *Journal,* "taking chances that no skier of his calibre would take unless something was terribly wrong or he was being pursued." The speaker was Bob Lee, a Portland mountaineer, who is a member of the exclusive international Alpine Club and who has led and advised U.S. expeditions to the Himalayas.

In his wild descent, Carter jumped several gaping crevices before going right off a steep canyon wall. Neither he nor his equipment was ever found.

Several of the seventy-five men in the search parties reported they experienced an uncomfortable feeling of being watched the whole time they were in the area. Lee said, "It was the most eerie experience I've ever had. I could feel the hair on my neck standing up ... I was unarmed except for my ice axe and, believe me, I never let go of that."

Lee said that both he and Dr. Otto Trott, the surgeon for the Seattle Mountain Rescue Council, came to the same conclusion: "The apes got him."

No doubt if the two detectives who accompanied Fred Beck and his companions into Ape Canyon had been presented with the story of Jim Carter, they would have said, "the bears got him." The bear of course is the first alternative offered by the cynical commentator: "Ah, come on, it must have been a big grizzly." But bears just do not fit the characteristics linked to the Sasquatch.

One of the best known and most respected grizzly bear hunters and big game guides in British Columbia, if not in all of North America, is Clayton Mack, a Bella Coola Indian from Anahim Lake in north-central B.C. Dahinden, accompanied by John Green, then a newspaperman and a partner in the Sasquatch hunt, talked with Clayton Mack shortly after the guide had seen unusual tracks during the winter of 1967. Mack said they were those of a biped and he dismissed any possibility of them belonging to a bear. He stated categorically that no bear moves about on two feet for any significant distance. Here's how he described the tracks:

"They weren't too big; a little bigger than my footprints. I took my shoes off and stepped alongside them. The fellow with me, Willie Schooner, said, 'It's a grizzly bear.' I said, 'No, it's got no front footprints, those are all hind prints.' Most of the prints were on top of logs, like he's moving along, but some were in between the logs and I could see real plain. It had been there just a few minutes before I got there because it was snowing, powder snow, and there was no fresh snow on top of the prints. When I came back into Bella Coola and told about it, a lot of people believed me; they know I wouldn't say I seen something if I didn't."

The discussion then took a new tack when the guide decided to elaborate on the Sasquatch and told of two personal experiences that until then he had related to no one.

"It was at the head of Gardner's Canal where we saw those tracks–and that's the same place where the thing came to the cabin that night....

"There was (a lawyer) from Hollywood, and (a doctor) from Jackson Hole, Wyoming, up here for bear. There was the three of us in the cabin, about two o'clock in the morning, when the thing yelled, right at the window. It yelled, like (making a sharp, harsh exhalation), '*Hargh*! *Haaargh*!' The lawyer jumped off the bed and shouted, 'What's that?'

31

I said, 'Well, we've been talking about Sasquatches, and I think that's one. Then it yelled down on the beach, then next thing up on the hill; just kept on going. Then daylight came and we went out bear-hunting. We came back and the float plane was supposed to pick us up so we waited on the beach. The lawyer said, 'I'm going to imitate that son of a gun,' and he did, and that son of a gun answered, just the same noise it had made at the window.''

Then Clayton Mack reached further into his past and told of the time he saw a Sasquatch on the tidal flats. He was heading for nearby Kwatna Inlet in his small boat, sometime during the early 1940's.

"I saw this thing walking on the beach; a light brown colour, standing about eight to nine feet tall. I thought it was a big bear–but he didn't go down on his four legs. I was nosing right towards him but I was about four hundred yards away so I didn't get a good look at his face. I kept wondering because he didn't go down on his four legs. He was right on the edge of the water; he stood up straight and looked at me, then turned and walked up to the timber. Then halfway up to the driftwood logs he stopped and turned and looked at me, twisting his head round. I never seen a grizzly bear on its hind feet stand and twist round with just its head; they always turn the whole body, and they go down on four feet to do it. Then he went on and got to the logs and walked on top of them. He got to the timber– it's second-growth–and it looked as though he just reached out and spread the trees apart as he walked through them, young spruce and hemlock trees."

Mack said that as a child he had frequently heard stories from the older people about the Sasquatch, but had then never taken them very seriously. "But now I've been thinking I believe it," he concluded.

Clayton Mack has nothing to lose but his reputation by telling monster stories; it's his reputation that makes him his living. There's no indication that his reputation is anything but intact still.

The *Dsonoqua* (Cannibal Woman) and her son on a Kwakiutl totem pole.

Albert Ostman (right) tells René Dahinden a remarkable story of how he was kidnapped by an old male Sasquatch during a trip along the B.C. coast in 1924. Held captive for a week by a family of four Sasquatches, he finally made his escape with the help of a rifle and a tin of snuff.

1

Deputy sheriff Verlin Herrington of Gray's Harbor County, Washington, has provided one of the most explicitly detailed descriptions of the many night-sightings of the Sasquatch. His report was disputed by his superiors, but he stuck by his story to the last detail.

The Chapman cabin at Ruby Creek was left to the elements after the Chapman family abandoned it, following the experience of Mrs. Jeannie Chapman and her children in 1941 with a creature which all investigations show possessed all the characteristics of the mysterious Sasquatch

Sheriff Bill Closner of Skamania County, Washington, made the cast of this huge 22-inch fooprint that measured 7-1/2 inches across the ball of the foot and 4-1/2 inches at the heel.

René Dahinden poses beside a wood carving of the Sasquatch at Willow Creek. The sculpture is the work of Jim McClarin and fits the general description of the creature. It stands eight feet tall, has a shoulder width of 41 inches and feet measuring 8 inches by 10 inches.

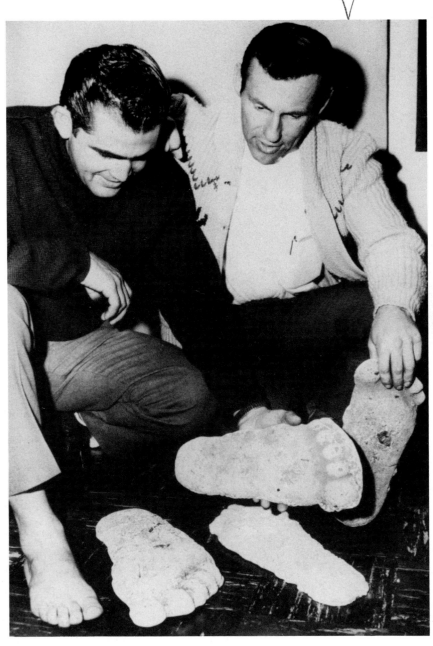

Bob Gimlin and Roger Patterson (right) examine plaster casts of some of the many prints left by the creature Patterson filmed at Bluff Creek in October 1967. The controversial film shows the creature fleeing along the creek bed and into the woods.

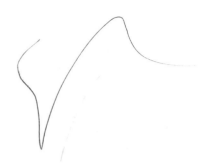

A frame from the Patterson film taken at Bluff Creek, of a creature believed to be the elusive Sasquatch. Subsequent scientific analyses have tended more and more to vindicate Patterson's claims that this film was genuine.

Just weeks before the Patterson film was taken in 1967, the Blue Creek Mountain area, near Bluff Creek, was the site of hundreds of gigantic footprints. This one measured 38.1 cm, slightly more than fifteen inches.

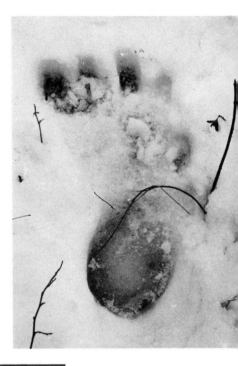

The right-foot print of an apparently crippled Sasquatch, one of a spread of 1,089 prints found in the small Washington community of Bossburg in 1969 that remain to this day among the most convincing tangible evidence of the Sasquatch.

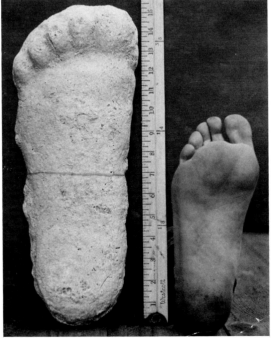

The plaster cast on the left was made from a footprint left by the creature filmed by Roger Patterson at Bluff Creek. It is more than fifteen inches long. Compare it with the size of Ren Dahinden's bare foot, right, a mere ten inches long.

The tracks of the mysterious creature on Powder Mountain went from stand to stand of balsam trees, apparently following the source of reachable food in the balsam buds. The trail continued for five miles before disappearing into ice caves at the foot of a glacier.

High school music teacher Richard Brown stands by the fence where he rested his scope-equipped rifle to follow the movements of a creature fitting the Sasquatch description, near The Dalles, Oregon in 1971. He watched for at least two minutes while the creature walked in full view across the meadow in the background.

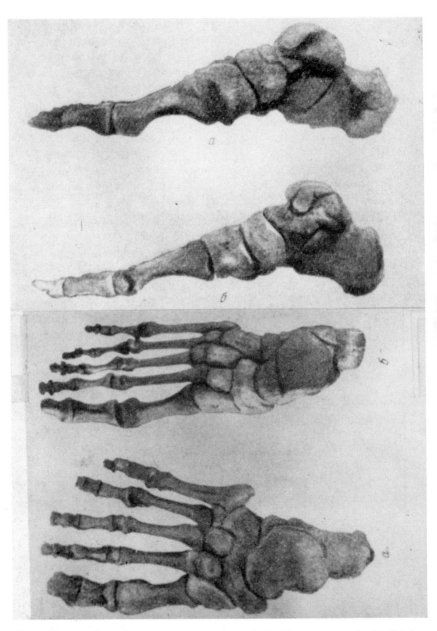

These pictures show (a) a reconstructed Neanderthal foot compared with (b) the foot of modern man, and illustrate the point made by Grover Krantz (Chapter 9) concerning the Sasquatch foot, and the relation of this to the heel of the creature in the Patterson film as put forward by the Russian researchers Bayanov and Bourtsev.

Igor Bourtsev displays a cast of the print found in the Pamir-Alai mountains in Tadzhikistan. The print measured 34 cm long (about 13 inches) and was 16 cm (about 6-1/4 inches) wide at the toes.

his sculpture, by Igor Bourtsev, is a
odel of the creature seen in the
atterson film.

The late Professor Boris Porshnev, a department head in the Institute of History of the Academy of Sciences of the U.S.S.R. in 1972 when this picture was taken. One of Russia's most highly esteemed historians and scientists, Porshnev spearheaded much important research into the question of the Russian equivalent of the Sasquatch, the Almas. He was convinced that his evidence indicated the probable existence of "the surviving remains of a branch of Neanderthals...in divers regions of the world."

Just after midnight on Sunday, March 15, 1987, in the snowbound oil-patch country near Dawson Creek, B.C., oil-rigger Myles Jack, shown here, and several of his colleagues, saw a creature that stood between seven and eight feet tall and weighed between 350 and 400 pounds. The creature's tracks supported Jack's claim that the creature took "huge steps–twice the length of that of the average man." (*Photo by Les Baszo,* The Province, *Vancouver*)

Sasquatch researcher Dennis Gates dons a gorilla costume to demonstrate the hoax in May 1977 that had many in the small city of Mission, B.C.–including the local RCMP–convinced that they had been visited by a Sasquatch.

René Dahinden stares out across the untouched miles of wooded, mountainous country in B.C.'s Garibaldi Park, "Sasquatch country." He has spent almost forty years searching for the truth about the Sasquatch and is determined to follow the mystery to its end.

Many stories of the Sasquatch have come from the Bella Coola area. Most of them are told by Indians–hardly surprising considering they make up most of the population. Cynics tend to dismiss the reports on the somewhat arbitrary and even racist grounds that they *are* from Indian sources, suggesting–in their more charitable moments–that folklore and booze have combined to weave an over-elaborate Saturday-night fantasy. The fact that the Indians generally keep the stories to themselves until pursued by people such as Dahinden seems to escape their reasoning.

After Dahinden had talked with Clayton Mack he was introduced to Harry Squiness who told of a happening while he was camped at Goose Point near Anahim Lake in 1963. Squiness was getting ready for sleep when the tent flap was opened from the outside and he saw what he described as a "monkey face, all covered with hair, with eyes like a man." Squiness grabbed for a flashlight, but it wasn't working. He then ran outside and tossed some gasoline on the embers of his camp fire. In the light that flared up he saw four man-ape-like creatures lying down, as though hiding, on the edge of his camp area about fourteen feet from his tent. As the flame rose, the four jumped up and walked away into the darkness, "walking like men." Squiness called to them: "Hey, what you doing out there? Hey, come back!" The creatures went off silently. Squiness checked for footprints but the grassy area held nothing. There was however the mark of one huge hand on a tree trunk and this he later showed to Clayton Mack.

Whatever the creatures were that Squiness saw, they scared him. He spent the night sitting up by his camp fire and the next morning he went into town and bought five boxes of 30.30 shells. He never saw the intruders again.

The Anahim Lake stories, like all other stories of face-to-face confrontations with the Sasquatch, could be chewed over endlessly, to little gain. Either one accepts them at face value, or one dismisses them as fabrications or mistakes. But let's not forget that Clayton Mack has not achieved the prestige he can boast as a woodsman, by making mistakes.

And before leaving Anahim Lake, it's worth noting that in the area there are several topographical features that bear as a prefix the word "Ape." Just south of Bella Coola there are Ape Lake, Ape Creek, Ape Glacier, and Ape Mountain. Their origin goes back beyond the map-making of the white man.

The word "Sasquatch" is a distillation of several Indian names given the hairy giant—*Seeahtik, Wauk-Wauk, Te Sami'etl Soquwiam, Saskahevis*—and became commonly used by the Chehalis Indians of British Columbia's Fraser Valley, particularly around the area of the villages of Harrison and Agassiz. During this century the region has been the source of many reports of incidents concerning the creature, and most of them include a reference to the revival, apparently after a lull of a number of years, of the Sasquatch's interest in populated areas. Typical is a story that appeared in the Vancouver *Province* in March of 1934:

> The fearsome Sasquatch have returned. Indian women in the Chehalis reservation are watching their youngsters closely these days, keeping them indoors at night, terrifying them with stories their old folk used to tell, of hairy giants who came down from the mountains and kidnapped naughty children.
>
> Men of the tribe are keeping their rifles handy, watching for unusual movements in the forest, and when their dogs bark at night they leap from bed, run to the window and peer out, expectantly. For the Sasquatch have returned.
>
> There is no longer any doubt about it. Suspicions were aroused some time ago that the dreaded wild men of the Chehalis hills were on the prowl again. But there was no proof. And then, one night this week, Frank Dan *saw* a Sasquatch! Saw it with his own eyes, clearly. There is no doubt about it now. Ask Frank Dan.

Investigating the cause of the persistent barking of his dog at night, Dan, who lives near the Harrison River on the Chehalis reserve, came face to face with a hairy giant. The creature, according to his report, was nude, covered with a fluff of black hair from head to foot, except for a small space around the eyes. He is described as tall, muscular, and of ferocious aspect.

After one look Frank ran into the house and secured the door. The giant, undisturbed, strode leisurely into the nearby bush and disappeared.

This is the third occasion that this individual has been reported seen here in the last ten months by two different persons.

These reputed hairy creatures are said by Indians to be the remnant of a race who lived on this continent ages ago and are referred to by them as "Sasquatch" or hairy mountain men....

Indians declare that until thirty years ago, several of these hairy creatures, men and women, were often encountered on the Harrison River and Chehalis reserve. An Indian woman states that when her husband was returning from Morris Creek with a score of ducks he had shot, a Sasquatch stepped out of the bush and took the ducks from him–except one, which the giant stuffed into the shirt of the frightened Indian....

The first thing to consider about this story is that the somewhat breathless prose is that of the writer, not of the Indians involved. One can easily shoot holes in the report; take the duck hunter for example: maybe he was just a lousy shot, maybe the hunting had been awful, or maybe he had dawdled away his day in pursuits he would rather not have had his wife know about. What a God-given alibi he had in the Sasquatch. Certainly it would be a tough one to argue. And there's the element of the "Bogey Man" stories which mothers all over the world use to chasten and persuade young children. On the other hand, such stories are rarely supported by the fathers to the extent of keeping a loaded weapon at the ready. One has to consider there was good cause for such precautions.

Frank Dan's encounter provoked the older people on the reserve to recall earlier days when the Sasquatch was apparently encountered with some regularity. Such a tale was recorded by a man known simply as Old Charlie:

"I was hunting in the mountains beyond Hatzic. I had my dog with me. I came out on a flat where there were several large cedar trees. The dog stood before one of the big trees and began to growl and bark. He was a clever dog. On looking up to see what was the trouble I noticed a large hole in the tree seven or eight feet from the ground. The dog pawed and leaped up on the trunk and looked at me to lift him up, which I did, and he went into the hole and then I heard a cry inside. I said to myself, 'the dog is tearing into a bear,' and I stood with my rifle ready. I called to ... the dog to drive him out, and out came something I took for a bear in my excitement. I shot and the thing fell to the ground. I was horrified to find I had shot a naked boy. However he was not badly hurt.

"Then out of the bushes stepped the strangest and the wildest creature I ever saw. I raised my rifle, not to shoot but to defend myself if necessary. The hairy creature, for that was what it was, walked fearlessly towards me. The wild creature was a woman, her face was almost black, and her hair swept to her waist. She was a giant in height–at least six feet and built in proportion. She looked savagely at me and then picked up the wounded boy and vanished."

People such as Old Charlie attributed nothing of the supernatural to their stories of the Sasquatch. They were well acquainted with the wild life of their region, depending as they did for their livelihood on hunting. They took their encounters with any creature for what they were, and related them to outsiders–always at the outsiders' instigation–with a minimum of embroidery and dramatization. They had no reason to want to "sell" the story.

The earlier reference to the Indian belief that the Sasquatches are "the remnant of a race who lived on this continent ages ago..." has given rise to at least one theory as to their origins; that is the story of the Karankawas. When the white man arrived in North America the Karankawas, reputed to be the most primitive of native peoples, held a long strip of territory between Galveston and Corpus Christi, Texas. They were said to be giants, fearless and efficient hunters who thrived on a diet of seafood and various roots and nuts. They functioned at a level little different to that of animals. With the arrival of the Europeans, the Karankawas were pushed back from their fertile territory. They fought many fierce battles with the encroaching pioneers but the new arrivals' sophisticated weaponry was more than they could handle.

The whites attempted to "save" the Karankawas by way of the ubiquitous missionary, but the efforts served only to further enrage the tribe. In 1688, the Karankawas took part in an attack which destroyed the La Salle settlement at Old Fort St. Louis in Jackson County, Texas and aroused the wrath of the settlers, who thereupon started a continuing vendetta which gradually drove the primitive giants from their land.

Eventually all trace of them disappeared, leaving us with the question of whether they found their way to the Northwest, and in sufficient numbers to propagate their race until the present time.

And a theory once common and still held by some is that the Sasquatch is indeed a primitive native tribe that has managed to avoid discovery. On first thought that may seem somewhat far-fetched, but it need not necessarily be. For the argument we have to go back to the small town of Oroville, in northern California. There, in the early morning of August 29, 1911, in a slaughter-house corral, a man–an Indian–was discovered cowering by the rail fence. This was Ishi, the last of the stone-age Yahi tribe. Forty years before, the last small group of his tribe had conceded the uselessness of fighting the white man and had disappeared into the nearby mountains. For a decade they lived undetected, then in desperation they began to raid homesteads for food. They did this for another ten years, in which time they were seen only once. In the mid-1890's the last five settled on a piece of land less than one and a half miles in area. They lived there, in permanent homes, lighting fires for cooking and for cremating their dead, for fifteen years without knowledge of the white man. When Ishi, the last of his people, huddled down by the corral fence, he had lived for thirty-nine years on the border of civilization but completely unknown to it.

This is by no means an attempt to make a case for the Sasquatch as a lost tribe of native North Americans; what it is will be known when one is captured or killed. The case of Ishi is simply used to demonstrate the potential for concealment–for any animal or being, but especially for those equipped to live off the land–in the areas that we are dealing with. It might be argued: "But that was in 1911; look how far man has moved in the country since then." And it would be a weak argument. The populated areas of the Pacific Northwest are in pockets and in strips, bordered by hundreds of thousands of square miles of territory that is, to put it mildly, inhospitable to man. British Columbia, for example, has an area of 366,000 square miles (as much as the combined area of the states of California, Washington, Oregon, and half of Idaho; or almost four times the area of Great Britain and Northern Ireland) and a population of little more than two million. Perhaps this also provides at least a partial answer to those skeptics (cynics would be the better word perhaps) who continually cry: "But if there are Sasquatches, why hasn't one been caught?"

Ishi was found near Oroville. One of the Sasquatch confrontations we will examine (Chapter 7)–and which is one of the more impressive in René Dahinden's files–also occurred near Oroville. We attach no particular significance to this, but mention it as an interesting coincidence.

Perhaps the "lost tribe" theory is a fanciful one, which orthodox science would consider at least flimsy. But should it be found to be valid, the occasion would not be the first on which the halls of science have rung with the sound of surprise. A few such examples will serve to close this chapter.

Reports of the African mountain gorilla were scoffed at by scientists for two hundred years before, only in 1902, they accepted it as established. The coelacanth, a fossil fish considered extinct for seventy million years, was caught in 1938 off South Africa, and others have been caught since. The largest known lizard in the world, the Komodo dragon, was discovered only in 1912, and the giant panda was once thought extinct for decades. The world's second-bulkiest land animal–Cotton's wide-lipped rhinoceros–was not found until 1910. And it was only in the early 1970s that people living in stone-age conditions were discovered in the Philippines.

Perhaps Grover Krantz, the anthropologist mentioned in connection with the story of Jacko, puts the scientific attitude into perspective when he says, in relation to the oddities of the world: "The giraffe. Now there's an unlikely creature. Scientists would deny its existence until one stepped on them."

So may it be with the Sasquatch.

CHAPTER 2

The following is part of a form letter written by Don Abbott, Curator of Archeology at the British Columbia provincial museum. He apparently was provoked into adopting the standard-reply form after a deluge of requests for his opinion followed his involvement in the Bluff Creek tracks episode in 1967 (See Chapter 6). The letter, as well as illustrating the enigma that the Sasquatch has become, suggests the dilemma that many scientists find themselves in because of it.

First, Mr. Abbott emphasizes that his field is archeology, "...not physical anthropology or primatology (the scientific disciplines most appropriate to the Sasquatch phenomenon if these beings should exist, or psychology or sociology if they should not). I am not an expert on the subject of Sasquatches, have never posed as one, and have no ambition to become one...."

The letter continues: "I am able to verify personally that the Bigfoot footprints which have been reported, or at least some of them, do occur.... (The tracks) are unquestionably either a deliberate hoax or else what they purport to be. They are certainly not the tracks of bear or any other creatures. Here too the experts are divided, with the majority rejecting them because of their flat, generally featureless appearance, unduly short toes, and other factors (Napier provides an interesting contrast to this in Chapter 9). At this point I would much prefer to join in the rejection (and my life would be much simpler if I did), but in all honesty there are a number of facts about these and similar sets of footprints which continue to bother me and which no one has been able to explain away to my satisfaction. These include (1) the depth of impression seeming to indicate a great body weight or else the force applied by some heavy machine (2) the apparent naturalness of the walk over several hundred yards including steps over logs and up banks (which would seem to eliminate the possibility of the prints being made by any type of machine of which I can readily conceive) (3) the number of reports of the occurrence of such tracks, their wide range in space and time, and the absolute remoteness of some of the areas where they have said to have been encountered, which would suggest that if these are the works of hoaxers these people must have a remarkably large and sophisticated organization and probably a good deal of money. No one has ever been caught faking Bigfoot prints to my knowledge." (Considering the fact that reports of the prints cover the area from Alaska to South America, and the time from the early 1800's to today, Mr. Abbott's reserve about hoaxers is a gem of understatement.) He continues:

"Reports of sightings would seem to be the least satisfactory line of evidence and it is likely that some of them could be attributed variously to lies, hallucinations or mistaken identifications. There remains however a sizeable core of people claiming to have seen Sasquatches who are apparently sober, reliable, and knowledgeable. There is a rather surprising degree of conformity, furthermore, to many of their descriptions. For this reason, too, then, I am no longer able to reject out of hand the possibility of Sasquatches existing.

"In summary, while I am not a 'believer' in Sasquatches, I am aware of certain phenomena which have not yet been adequately explained if these rather unlikely creatures do not, in fact, exist. It may well be that all of these phenomena, including many of the reported sightings, are part of a gigantic hoax. It may also be that belief in this creature on the part of many people is supported by a mixture of many independent hoaxes, coincidences, and misinterpretations, cemented together by wishful thinking.

From present perspectives these sorts of explanations seem fairly incredible. On the other hand the existence of a giant non-human bipedal primate as part of the fauna of western North America is totally unacceptable to the great majority of competent scientists...."

Mr. Abbott's statement is at the same time a cautious and a courageous one. At a time (the late 1960's) when most scientists were dismissing the subject with various versions of Dr. T.D. Stewart's "bosh," he at least was conceding that there was "something" out there, and that it wasn't a bear. On the matter of a possible hoax, apart from the almost unbelievably complex logistics that would be involved, Mr. Abbott might have pointed out that the hoaxers, especially any involved in the many sightings of the creatures, would have stood a better than even chance of collecting a fatal dose of lead from large-calibre rifles as they trotted about in their fur suits. Perhaps he is not fully familiar with the death toll that characterizes hunting season in the Pacific Northwest, when anything that moves, let alone anything that resembles wildlife, is fair game.

We have already considered some of what Mr. Abbott calls "the sizeable core of people ... who are apparently sober, reliable and knowledgeable," and their stories. There are many others whose stories are well worth considering, all of whom were sought out by René Dahinden and their experiences recorded.

John X is a prospector working for a Vancouver mining company. His is the only case in which the individual's name will not be used. He insists on this because of what he fears would be his employer's attitude should he be identified. The incident took place on June 28, 1965, when John X and his brother were prospecting in the Pitt Lake area, about twenty-five to thirty miles northeast of Vancouver. This is his story:

"We were hiking into a valley about noon when we ran into these tremendous footprints that went down to a small stream that was frozen over. The ice had been broken and then the footprints led back up again, away from it. We spent some time studying the prints because of their size. They were twice the length of my boot, which would make them twenty-four inches long, and the width across the base of the toes was twelve inches. The distance between the footprints was twice my stride, and their depth in the snow was about two inches. You could tell the right foot from the left because of the bulbous big toes. We went on up the valley–and then, looking across a small frozen pond we could see this creature. We both figured the thing was between ten and twelve feet tall (this is one of the bigger estimates of the thing's size, but not the biggest: see Chapter 7, concerning the Big Horn Dam incident). It was covered in auburn hair, the head was close to the shoulders and seemed to have fairly long and very much darker hair than the rest of it. The arms were longer than a human's, seeming to come below the knee. When we saw it, it was within a city-block length of us, at about the same height as us on the opposite side of the valley.

"The hands were huge–they reminded me of our canoe paddle–and they were open; they appeared to be a yellowish colour. We spent some time watching the creature; in fact we both had a chocolate bar and a cigarette while we watched. It just stood, transferring its weight from one foot to the other, which gave it a kind of rocking motion, and its hands seemed to go back and forth as it moved.

"It didn't seem to be ferocious or anything so we just stayed and watched it for a while, then we carried on up the valley. We were in the valley approximately four and a half hours. When we came down again it had gone and we returned to our base camp. The following day we took off up to a meadow, and there we saw footprints smaller than the ones we saw the day before. Up there also was a small pond and something had broken the ice in the middle of it–and these prints went right out to the middle of the pond, and then were visible on the far side of it.

"The features of the creature we saw that first day appeared to be flat, but we were looking straight on so this is hard to tell. But we did have a good view: it was noon and the sun was fairly close to the top. It was a clear day; there was no way you could make a mistake as far as the creature itself was concerned. There was a way out of the valley, behind where the creature was, and I'm surmising that's where it went."

John X concluded that part of his story by saying: "I was as close as I would like to have been without a rifle."

Three days later he flew back into the area in a helicopter in the company of a reporter from the Vancouver *Sun:*

"We both took pictures (of the tracks). We also flew over another area and saw tracks going along the crest of the mountain and down over a cliff and on to a ledge about twenty feet below. It didn't seem as though there had been much of a problem for the thing getting down that cliff, and this would discount a bear as far as I'm concerned. And, having seen the creature, I know that its reach would have been sufficient to let it down that far easily."

The prospector's story was never published in the Vancouver *Sun* because he would not permit his name to be used. Consequently he paid for the rental of the helicopter. He explained that his job consisted of going out into the field, writing reports of his findings, and having these reports accepted by mining companies. He said: "They consider that what I say is so, is so, and if they had read about this, and I had no real proof, they would tend to think I was not a responsible person."

John X sounds like a responsible person. He does not sound like someone with a kink for playing hoaxes. There seems to be no good reason for him to have invented such a story, no reason not to believe that he saw what he says he saw.

Another whose job consists—or did consist—to a great extent of being a careful witness to his day's work was Verlin Herrington, a deputy sheriff of Gray's Harbor County, Washington State. He relates an incident that occurred in the early morning of Sunday July 27, 1969–the year that Dahinden refers to as The Biggest Year. It would be hard to find a more sober approach than Herrington's in the tape-recorded interview he held with Dahinden. Listening to it is like listening to the dutiful reading of a regular police report–which, in effect, it was. Unfortunately for Herrington though, it received anything but a regular response from his superiors.

Herrington tells his story:

"I had been on a detail and was on my way back to my residence (at Copalis Beach). This was at 2.35 a.m. of July 27th, 1969. As I came around a slight curve in the road I spotted a large hairy creature standing in the middle of the road. I thought at first it was a bear looking for her cubs. As I drew nearer–my lights must have been blinding it–I realized it wasn't going to move. I put on my brakes and came to a halt, then I coasted on up to about eighty-five to ninety feet away from her. The thing was standing in a kind of stooped position, startled, watching my vehicle. I came to a complete stop, got my spotlight out and turned it on the animal, at which point it walked to the side of the road, still in a startled posture, and stood there for a moment. I noticed that its eyes had glowed yellow in the spotlight. I rolled my car window down, drew my pistol, and got out of the vehicle. I realized that it was something other than a bear and I decided I would shoot it and would then have a trail to follow; I hoped to get one shot, maybe in the leg, then get out of there and come back in the morning and track it. But as I cocked my pistol it went out of the spotlight and into the woods. I got into my car and left."

Herrington then expanded on his description of the thing: "I was having to adjust the spotlight the whole time and I did spot it on several places, so that I could see each detail fairly well. I would estimate its height at seven to eight feet and its weight at something over three hundred pounds. It had hair all over it of a dark brown colour, but the hair on its head was longer than that on the rest of its

46

body–between five and seven inches long. The first thing that startled me was it had breasts on it like those of a woman; they had hair on them also, except for the nipples which were black, like the thing's face. While it was standing I could see the back of one hand and the palm of another and I could distinguish fingers. It had legs like a human and buttocks like a human...."

The deputy was also able to distinguish the creature's feet and toes, which were also covered with hair. Before it moved off into the bush it took only four shuffling strides to cross the highway.

As he left the scene Verlin Herrington was aware that he had a problem; the same one that occurs to all those who happen on a Sasquatch: to tell, or not to tell. Finally: "Well, I believe that I'm a truthful man, so I decided to tell the other (deputies)."

In view of what eventually happened, he would have profited by keeping quiet. On his way home he called in at a café where two of his colleagues were having mid-shift coffee. He told them what he had seen and they made the predictable response of enjoying a good belly laugh. But he persisted, and they listened. Herrington was a respected member of the force, and he was not joking. As soon as it was light they went with him to the spot where they found, and photographed, several footprints, measuring eighteen inches by seven inches, clearly impressed in the soft soil on the road shoulder.

Had the incident been kept among the police officers it is likely that Verlin Herrington still would be a member of the Gray's Harbor County force. His intention had been to file a report and say nothing to anyone outside the police department. However, his discussions in the café had been overheard and next day the news of the sighting was spread far and wide on the teletypes of the wire services.

For what followed it's important to remember that the position of sheriff–not deputy–in the U.S. is an elected position. If the voters don't like what you do during one term behind the silver badge, you won't serve another one. The press coverage and badgering of the incident grew to the point where, apparently, the Gray's Harbor County sheriff judged it a threat to his security; after all, he was the one who had hired Herrington. He issued a denial of the story, declaring that Herrington had changed his mind and that what he had seen had, after all, been a bear.

For our records, let it be noted that Dahinden interviewed the deputy several days *after* the sheriff had issued his statement. And for the records of those who see a Sasquatch in the future, let it be noted that Verlin Herrington was not re-hired as a deputy sheriff the following year. He took a job with the parks service, and he's still sticking to his story.

Another man who sticks with his story is William Roe. So impressed by his experience was this former trapper that he went to the extent of swearing out an affidavit before a Justice of the Peace. In Canada this is no trivial thing (the deposition says: "...knowing that it is of the same force and effect as if made under oath and by virtue of the Canada Evidence Act.") and the man who would pursue that course must, one would speculate, be listened to closely. The following is the text of the affidavit sworn on August 26, 1957, before W.H. Clarke, a commissioner for oaths in Edmonton, Alberta.

"Ever since I was a small boy back in the forests of Michigan I have studied the lives and habits of wild animals. Later when I supported my family in northern Alberta by hunting and trapping, I spent many hours just observing the wild things. They fascinated me. But the most incredible experience I ever had with a wild creature occurred near a little town called Tete Jaune Cache, British Columbia, about eighty miles west of Jasper, Alberta.

"I had been working on the highway near Tete Jaune Cache for about two years. In October, 1955, I decided to climb five miles up Mica Mountain to an old deserted mine, just for something to do. I came in sight of the mine about three o'clock in the afternoon after an easy climb. I had just come out of a patch of low brush into a clearing when I saw what I thought was a grizzly bear in the brush on the other side. I had shot a grizzly near that spot the year before. This one was only about seventy-five yards away, but I didn't want to shoot it for I had no way of getting it out. So I sat down on a small rock and watched, my rifle in my hands.

"I could just see part of the animal's head and the top of one shoulder. A moment later it raised up and stepped out into the opening. Then I saw it was not a bear.

"This, to the best of my recollection, is what the creature looked like and how it acted as it came across the clearing directly toward me. My first impression was of a huge man, about six feet tall, almost three feet wide, and probably weighing somewhere near three hundred pounds. It was covered from head to foot with dark brown silver-tipped hair. But as it came closer I saw by its breasts that it was female.

"And yet its torso was not curved like a female's. Its broad frame was straight from shoulder to hip. Its arms were much thicker than a man's arms and longer, reaching almost to its knees. Its feet were broader proportionately than a man's, about five inches wide at the front and tapering to much thinner heels. When it walked it placed the heel of its foot down first, and I could see the grey-brown skin or hide on the soles of its feet.

"It came to the edge of the bush I was hiding in, within twenty feet of me, and squatted down on its haunches. Reaching out its hands, it pulled the branches of bushes toward it and stripped the leaves with its teeth. Its lips curled flexibly around the leaves as it ate. I was close enough to see that its teeth were white and even.

"The shape of this creature's head somewhat resembled a Negro's (sic). The head was higher at the back than at the front. The nose was broad and flat. The lips and chin protruded farther than its nose. But the hair that covered it, leaving bare only the parts of its face around the mouth, nose and ears, made it resemble an animal as much as a human. None of this hair, even on the back of its head, was longer than an inch, and that on its face much shorter. Its ears were shaped like a human's ears. But its eyes were small and black like a bear's. And its neck was also unhuman; thicker and shorter than any man's I had ever seen.

"As I watched this creature I wondered if some movie company was making a film at this place and if what I saw was an actor, made up to look partly human and partly animal. But as I observed it more I decided it would be impossible to fake such a specimen. Anyway, I learned later that there was no such company near that area. Nor in fact did anyone live up Mica Mountain, according to the people who lived in Tete Jaune Cache.

"Finally the wild thing must have got my scent for it looked directly at me through an opening in the brush. A look of amazement crossed its face. It looked so comical at the moment I had to grin. Still in a crouched position it backed up three or four short steps, then straightened up to its full height and started to walk rapidly back the way it had come. For a moment it watched me over its shoulder as it went, not exactly afraid, but as though it wanted no contact with anything strange.

"The thought came to me that if I shot it, I would possibly have a specimen of great interest to scientists the world over. I had heard stories about the Sasquatch, the giant hairy Indians (sic) that live in the legends of British Columbia Indians, and also many claim are still in fact alive today. Maybe this was a Sasquatch, I told myself.

"I levelled my rifle. The creature was still walking rapidly away, again turning its head to look in my direction. I lowered the rifle. Although I have called the creature 'it,' I felt now that it was a human being and I knew I would never forgive myself if I killed it.

"Just as it came to the other patch of bush it threw its head back and made a peculiar noise that seemed to be half laugh and half language, and which I can only describe as

50

a kind of whinny. Then it walked from the small brush into a stand of lodge-pole pine.

"I stepped out into the opening and looked across a small ridge just beyond the pine to see if I could see it again. It came out on the ridge a couple of hundred yards away from me, tipped its head back again, and again emitted the only sound I had heard it make, but what this half-laugh, half-language was meant to convey, I do not know. It disappeared then and I never saw it again.

"I wanted to find out if it lived on vegetation entirely or (if it) ate meat as well, so I went down and looked for signs (droppings). I found it in five different places, and though I examined it thoroughly, could find no hair or shells of bugs or insects. So I believe it was strictly a vegetarian.

"I found one place where it had slept for a couple of nights under a tree. Now the nights were cool up the mountain, at this time of the year especially, and yet it had not used a fire. I found no sign that it possessed even the simplest of tools, nor a single companion while in this place.

"Whether this creature was a Sasquatch I do not know. It will always remain a mystery to me unless another one is found.

"I hereby declare the above statement to be in every part true, to the best of my powers of observation and recollection."

Roe's story rings true. The details he stresses would be those which experienced woodsmen and students of wild-life would notice. He draws no dramatic conclusions; simply reports what he saw. No one asked Roe to swear the affidavit and he sought no publicity after he did swear it–though the story got out, as stories of such things always will. Either William Roe is a liar, or he was hallucinating up on Mica Mountain–or he saw a Sasquatch.

René Dahinden's judgment has been called on to measure some unusual tales. And none more unusual than the one that follows, and which was brought to his attention as a direct outcome of the William Roe story. It's a story told by Albert Ostman, a retired logger, interviewed in Fort Langley, British Columbia. His response on hearing of the Roe incident was (and here I paraphrase): "Saw one? Hell, I was kidnapped by one and lived with four of the damned things!"

The Ostman story has long been a favourite item for those writing magazine or newspaper pieces on the Sasquatch, whether of a serious or whimsical nature. It was first told in full to René and John Green, the one-time newspaperman and Sasquatch hunter, in a long interview. The complete text of that interview appears in Green's booklet: *On The Track of The Sasquatch.* In presenting it for examination here I have condensed areas that appear to be outside of the main issue: the kidnapping and the events leading up to the escape.

The story briefly is that he was kidnapped by a male Sasquatch and held captive for a week before escaping– using a box of snuff as his key. In later discussions with René (who has been back to Ostman at least a dozen times since the initial interview), Ostman hints strongly that he was taken for stud purposes, suggesting that the old man wanted him for a mate for the daughter. As it was, Ostman wasn't with them long enough to find out whether his theory had any foundation.

We have to go back to 1924, when Ostman, having just completed a year on heavy construction work, decided he needed a vacation. He picked on the fiord-like coast of B.C., more than a hundred miles north of Vancouver, specifically, Toba Inlet, from where stories of a lost gold mine had circulated. He would combine the holiday with a casual search for the mine.

He hired as a guide an old Indian, who intrigued him with stories of a white man who had regularly brought gold out of the area until he failed to come out after his last trip. The Indian speculated that the white man had been killed by a Sasquatch. Ostman said he had never heard of the things and, when the Indian described them for him, concluded that he didn't believe they existed anyway.

At the head of the inlet, Ostman made camp and told the Indian to be there to meet him in three weeks. Among his supplies Ostman had a 30-30 Winchester rifle, and several tins of snuff. He stashed some of the goods in a biscuit tin and took the rest, and his sleeping bag, with him. For about a week he trekked up and down hill and valley, shooting a deer for meat on one occasion, a squirrel and a grouse on others. And then, as he says, "things started to happen."

On waking he noticed that some of his equipment had been disturbed, though there was nothing missing:

"That night I filled up the magazine of my rifle. I still had one full box of twenty shells in my pocket, besides a full magazine and six shells in my coat pocket. That night I laid my rifle under the edge of my sleeping bag. I thought a porcupine had visited me the night before and porkies like leather, so I put my shoes in the bottom of my sleeping bag.

"Next morning my pack sack had been emptied out. Someone had turned the sack upside down. It was still hanging on the pole from the shoulder straps as I had hung it up. Then I noticed one half of a packet of prunes was missing. Also my pancake flour was missing. But my salt bag was not touched. Porkies always look for salt, so I decided that it must be something else but porkies. I looked for tracks but found none. I did not think it was a bear, they always tear up and make a mess of things. I kept close to camp now in case the visitor would come back."

The visits went on for three nights. Ostman didn't want to move his camp site as he had found good protection from the weather, and a good spring for water. The rest of his story follows.

"This night it was cloudy and looked like it might rain. I took special notice of how everything was arranged. I closed my pack sack. I did not undress–I just took off my shoes and put them in the bottom of my sleeping bag. I drove my prospecting pick into one of the trees so I could reach it from my bed. I also put the rifle alongside me, inside the sleeping bag. I fully intended to stay awake all night to find out who my visitor was, but I must have fallen asleep.

"I was awakened by something picking me up. I was half asleep and at first didn't remember where I was. As I began to get my wits together I remembered I was on a prospecting trip and in my sleeping bag. My first thought was that it must be a snow slide, but there was no snow around. Then I felt like I was being tossed on horseback, but I could feel that whatever it was, was walking.

"I tried to reason what kind of animal this could be. I tried to get at my sheath knife to cut my way out, but I was in an almost sitting position and the knife was under me; I could not get hold of it. But the rifle was in front of me; I had a good hold on that and had no intention of letting it go. At times I could feel my pack sack touching me and could feel the cans in it touching my back.

"After about an hour I could feel we were going up a steep hill. I could feel myself rise with every step. What was carrying me was breathing hard and sometimes it gave a slight cough. Now I knew this must be one of the mountain Sasquatch giants the Indian told me about.

"I was in a very uncomfortable position, unable to move. I was sitting on my feet and one of my boots was crossed with the hobnail sole up across my foot. It hurt me terribly but I could not move. It was very hot inside. It was lucky for me that this fellow's hand was not big enough to close up the whole bag when he picked me up (there was a small opening at the top), otherwise I would have suffocated.

"Now he was going downhill. I could feel myself touching the ground at times and once he dragged me behind him.... Then he seemed to get on level ground and was moving at a trot for a long time. By now I had cramps in my legs and the pain was terrible. I was wishing he would get to his destination soon. I could not stand this kind of transportation much longer.

"Now he was going uphill again and it didn't hurt me so much. I tried to estimate distance and directions; as near as I could guess we were about three hours travelling. I had no idea what time he started as I was asleep when he picked me up.

"Finally he stopped and let me down, then he dropped my pack sack–I could hear the cans rattle. Then I heard chattering, some kind of talk I didn't understand. The ground was sloping, so when he let go my sleeping bag I rolled headfirst downhill. I got my head out and got some air. I tried to straighten my legs and crawl out, but my legs were numb. It was still dark, I couldn't see what my captors looked like. I tried to massage my legs, to get some life into them, and to get my shoes on. I realized now there were four of them. They were standing around me and chattering. I had never heard of Sasquatch before the Indian told me about them, but I knew now I was right among them.

"But how to get away from them–that was another question. I began to see the outline of them now as it got lighter ... I got my boots out from the sleeping bag and tried to stand up. I was wobbly on my feet but had a good hold of my rifle.

"I asked: 'What do you fellows want with me?' There was only some more chatter. It was getting lighter now and I could make out the forms of four people.... They looked like a family: old man, old lady, and two younger ones, a boy and a girl. The boy and the girl seemed scared of me and the old lady did not seem too pleased with what the old man had dragged home. But the old man was waving his arms and telling them all what he had in mind. They all left me then.

"I had my compass and my prospecting glass ... I tried to reason our location, and where I was. I could see that I was in a small valley or basin of about ten acres, surrounded by high mountains. On the southeast there was a V-shaped opening, about eight feet wide at the bottom and about twenty feet high at the highest point. That must be the way

I came in. But how would I get out? The old man was sitting near the opening now. I moved my belongings up close to the west wall. There were two small cypress trees there and these would do for a shelter for the time being–until I found out what these people want with me, and how to get away from there."

Ostman took stock of his supplies. He had canned meat and vegetables, coffee, milk, hardtack and butter. He had his rifle with a full magazine and six extra shells–the full box had disappeared during the trip–and his sheath knife. He emptied the coffee from its can into a small towel, and took the can to look for water, finding a spring and filling the can:

"When I got back the young boy was looking over my belongings, but he didn't touch anything. On the way back I noticed where these people were sleeping. On the east wall of this valley was a shelf in the mountain side with overhanging rock, about ten feet deep and thirty feet wide. The floor was covered with lots of dry moss and they had some kind of blankets woven of narrow strips of cedar bark packed with dry moss. They looked very practical and warm...."

For two days Ostman pondered on how to escape. While he gave it thought he managed to interest the young boy and girl in the snuff box that was to play a vital part in his escape. On the second day he made a determined move to the opening in the valley wall but the old man, with calls of what sounded like *"Soaka, Soaka,"* pushed him back. He considered shooting his way out, but then wondered if his fire power was enough to cope with the bulk of his captors.

He noticed that the older female–" a meek old thing"– went out collecting food: "...grass and twigs of all kinds as well as some kind of nuts that grow in the ground," and that the young boy helped her in this. He continued to give the youngster, and finally the old man, samples of snuff, which apparently was much enjoyed. Ostman's stated aim was to eventually give the old man such a dose of snuff to eat that it would kill him and thus, Ostman reasoned, the death would be unintentional suicide and not murder.

Ostman described their body sizes and shapes, pointing out than the girl had a flat chest, "...no development like young ladies." The young male he estimated was about seven feet tall, weighed around three hundred pounds, and had a fifty-fifty-five inch chest and about a thirty-six inch waist:

"He had wide jaws and a narrow forehead that slanted upward to the back where the head was round. The hair on their heads was about six inches long, that on the rest of their bodies was shorter and thick. The womens' hair was a bit longer on their heads and the hair on their forehead had an upward turn–like what they call bangs today.

"The old lady was about seven feet tall and would weigh between five hundred and fifty and six hundred pounds. She had wide hips and a goose-like walk. She was not built for beauty or speed. Some of those brassieres and uplifts would have made a great improvement to her looks and figure.

"The old man must have been nearly eight feet tall. His eyeteeth were longer than the rest of the teeth, but not long enough to be called tusks. He had a barrel chest and a big hump on his back and powerful shoulders. His biceps were enormous and his forearms were longer than most people would have, but well proportioned. He had long, broad, hands but his fingers were short in proportion. His finger-nails were like chisels.

"The only place they had no hair was inside their hands, on the soles of their feet, and on the upper part of the nose and the eyelids. I never saw the ears; they were covered with hair."

He describes the boy's sole as being "padded like a dog's foot" and stresses the size and strength of the big toe which, he says, was the boy's main agent of purchase in climbing rock faces.

The creatures sat by bending their knees out and coming straight down, and stood by rising straight up without any use of the hands or arms.

Ostman judged the creatures to be nomadic, their movements geared to food supplies in given spots. He stressed their dependence upon roots, twigs and grasses, saying he never saw them eat meat.

His moment for escape came one morning, a week after his abduction, when both males were drawn to a fire he lit (the first time he had done so while there) to make coffee. He enjoyed his coffee and some buttered hardtack, then drew out his snuff box and pinched off enough for a comfortable chewing session. The old man reached out for the box; Ostman offered it but held tight, supposing the old man would also take just a polite portion. Instead, he grabbed the box, tipped it up and swallowed the contents, then licked the box inside for the remainder:

"After a few minutes his eyes began to roll over in his head and he was looking straight up. I could see he was sick. Then he grabbed my coffee can which was quite cold by this time and emptied that in his mouth, grounds and all. That did no good. He stuck his head between his legs and rolled forward a few times away from me. Then he began to squeal like a stuck pig.

"I grabbed my rifle. I said to myself, 'This is it; if he comes for me I'll shoot him plumb between the eyes.' But he wanted water, he started for the spring. I packed my sleeping bag in my pack sack with the few cans I had left. The young fellow had run over to his mother, and she had started to squeal. I started for the opening in the wall, and I just made it. The old lady was right behind me. I fired one shot over her head."

Ostman was not followed, and soon, coming over a ridge, he saw Mt. Baker off to the south and knew he had his directions. Later that day he shot a blue grouse, made camp, and roasted the bird for his supper. He blamed the bird for the lousy feeling he had when he woke the next day. Exhausted and ill he pressed on that following day and, after six or seven hours of strenuous hiking, he heard the sound of a donkey engine working at a logging operation. He staggered out of the bush, startling the loggers on the job.

"I told them I was a prospector and was lost ... I didn't like to tell them I had been kidnapped by a Sasquatch because if I had, they probably would have said I was crazy."

The loggers fed Ostman and generally put him to rights before sending him off on his way in a logging truck to their main camp. From there he went down to the Salmon Arm branch of the Sechelt Inlet where he got the boat back to Vancouver.

He concludes his story:

"That was my last prospecting trip and my only experience with what is known as Sasquatches. I know that in 1924 there were four Sasquatches living. It might be only two now; the old man and the old lady might be dead by this time."

That's how René and John Green heard it. And that's how René has heard it over and over again, with never a shift in the smallest of detail. Green went back once after the first interview and took with him police magistrate and Justice of the Peace A.M. Naismith. The J.P. went right through Ostman's story, searching for a flaw in either that or in the man, and concluded he could find it in neither. That visit resulted in Ostman swearing the story on oath, in the way that Roe did, the document being authorized by Naismith.

The trouble with the Ostman story is that it's too good to be true–and by that I'm not saying that it's not true. It's difficult enough for us to accept the idea of the Sasquatch roaming the woods and hills, even though the evidence, if only of the footprints, says this is so. We can look at the prints and say, "well, yes, obviously it's out there, there are its damned feet." But that's the intellect at work. The emotions have yet to be convinced. So long as the thing remains at a distance, so long as it is the subject only of fleeting confrontations, we can cope with it–albeit somewhat nervously. But to accept Ostman's story unconditionally means taking the irreversible step of proclaiming the Sasquatch irrefutable. And that's an awfully big step. And what's more, it would spoil a good mystery.

Ostman's story provokes a number of questions. First, why would a man contain such an astonishing tale for more than thirty years? Could it be simply, as he says, that he feared the ridicule he knew would follow? And that once he realized that other people (i.e. Roe) were talking of their experiences, he had the confidence to relate it? Or do we have a case of a man, growing old, seeing behind him a life marked by nothing of any great note, jumping at a chance to leave something other than a grave marker for posterity? Ostman's wife and only daughter had both died within a few years of the family coming to Canada from Sweden. Could his subsequent preoccupation with his role as a potential propagator of the Sasquatch family be only an exercise in a mixture of nostalgic yearning and sexual fantasy? The story provokes the questions but provides no answers, only room for speculation.

In subsequent talks with René, Ostman made particular reference to the size of the old male Sasquatch's penis. He indicated that the head was hooded with skin and in this respect resembled that of a stallion–but only in this respect. He seemed puzzled by the fact that the old man's was only about two inches long. Now, if Ostman had been fantasizing about the Sasquatch family, it would seem logical that he would have endowed the male with much more impressive equipment than this, to match the rest of its giant stature. And the instance becomes even more interesting when we consider that the gorilla, the biggest of all known primates, itself has to make do with a penis of about two inches in length. To be cynical to the end, we would have to consider: did Ostman make a thorough study of

60

primate physiology, and then embark on his story? It seems unlikely.

Napier comments on the Roe and Ostman stories in his book, *Bigfoot*. His objection to the Ostman story concerns the Sasquatch food supply. In brief he points out that anything of the size of the creatures Ostman describes would need vastly more of the low-energy foods (the indigenous roots and grasses) than they apparently collected, to sustain them. He adds that the vegetation of the area produces the poorest of low-energy foods anyway. But this is not necessarily a convincing argument. The area supports a healthy breed of grizzly bear whose specimens have topped the thousand-pound mark. But grizzlies eat fish and insects and rodents, as well as vegetation, one might argue back. But then, according to many reports, so do Sasquatch. The fact that Ostman didn't see the creatures eating meat isn't final proof that they never did. The very fact that they had him there and wanted to keep him would provide one good reason for them not straying far in the hunt. Maybe they were prepared to sacrifice their stomachs for the period required to make a decision on Ostman, before he forestalled them. Maybe even, as Napier quips, "...Ostman himself represented the old man's contribution to the family larder."(!)

Napier draws some comparisons between the Ostman and Roe stories:

> When it walked, according to Roe's account, it placed its heel down first. This observation is of considerable relevance because the "heel-strike," as it is called, is characteristic of human walking or striding.
>
> (But) the special point of interest ... is first, the proportions of the female's body. According to Ostman's story, the hips of the female were very broad with the result that she could only manage a waddling gait; a logical enough extrapolation from structure to function. Roe, on the other hand, makes a strong point

61

of the absence of prominent hips in his female and of her human-like stride. One feels that they cannot both be right unless Roe's girl was really immature, which the prominence of the breasts seems to deny....

Well, that's probably sound anatomical reasoning. On the other hand, as anyone can tell you who has spent any time at all inspecting the girls of Vancouver on a pleasant summer's day, there's nothing that provides so much disparateness as the female form.

Anyway, the last word on the issue goes to Albert Ostman. He listens to René's and others' reservations, and says firmly: "I don't care a damn what you think."

CHAPTER 3

Although the most dramatic events involving Sasquatches in recent years have occurred—as subsequent chapters will show—in the United States, it's in British Columbia that Dahinden feels the most promising areas exist for pursuing the creature. And he points to the north central coast region (in the Bella Coola area) as the most likely spot, where thousands of square miles have never felt man's foot, and where the reasonably moderate climate combines with a plentiful food supply from beaches (B.C. has 16,900 miles of coastline), tidal rivers, and rain forests. And it's from B.C. that the majority of Sasquatch reports have come since the start of this century.

Apart from the Vancouver Island incidents, until the spate of sightings and footprints in the last ten to fifteen years in northern California, most of the reported events took place in the Harrison-Agassiz area. Just twelve miles east of Harrison, at Ruby Creek, an event occurred in 1941 which is something of a milestone for Sasquatch investigators. It was, according to records, the first voluntary visit by the creature to what we call civilization, and the first time that a substantial set of tracks was viewed by a number of persons from various walks of life, including a police official.

It was an afternoon in September. Mrs. Jeannie Chapman and her two young children, Jimmie and Rosie, were at home in their cabin near the railroad at Ruby Creek. The father, George Chapman, was at work as a section hand for the Canadian Pacific Railway, some way down the tracks.

Young Jimmie went out to play but within a few minutes came rushing back into the house, crying, "Mummy, there's a big cow coming out of the woods!" Mrs. Chapman went to the window and saw, striding across the field, an eight-foot tall human-like creature, walking easily erect. She grabbed Jimmie and hushed him, hurriedly put Rosie's shoes on the child, and waited. The man-giant veered away from the house and entered the lean-to at one side, where it started banging violently about. Jeannie Chapman grabbed the children, hustled them out of the house and fled towards the river and then along the river towards the Ruby Creek station. Halfway there she met her husband and the section gang. She was incoherent, hysterical with fear. The men calmed her down, took her to a relative's home, armed themselves with rifles, and headed for the cabin, confident they would find the tracks of a marauding bear. But no bear had made the prints they found near the Chapman home. They were sixteen inches long and eight inches wide at the ball of the foot and showed five clear toe impressions on each foot. The stride varied between four and five feet, and the print impressions were two inches deep in the soil on the Chapman's potato patch. The tracks went for half a mile and did not falter at a four-foot high fence, whatever had made the tracks taking the obstacle in its stride. The trail ended on rocky ground at the foot of Ruby Bluffs.

During the creature's investigation of the Chapman shed, it had found a fifty-five-gallon barrel of salted salmon, tasted it and, apparently not happy with the result, had tossed the barrel and its contents out into the yard. Then it had gone down to the river, presumably to wash the salt from its mouth. There was no indication that the creature had considered pursuing or harming the Chapman family.

All the men in the railway gang had little trouble deciding that the tracks were not those of a bear. All were regular hunters and accomplished woodsmen, quite familiar with the habits and markings of bears, which thrived in the area. The then deputy sheriff of neighbouring Whatcom County, Washington–Joe Dunn–visited the scene, inspected, measured and followed the tracks and concluded:

"I am well satisfied that these tracks are not those of a bear. They resemble those of a flat-footed (human) with broken arches." He added that he was thoroughly familiar with all kinds of bear tracks.

Gustav Tyfting, one of Chapman's workmates, and his wife, later made sworn statements concerning the nature of the tracks, pointing to the clear definition, the absence of claw marks or any indication that the creature had walked on all fours. And George Cousins, a telegraph operator at Ruby Creek at the time, also swore a statement in which he says the tracks were at least three times bigger than any bear tracks he had ever seen.

The Chapmans never returned to the cabin. Their lives ended in tragedy in 1959 when the whole family was drowned while crossing the Fraser at night in a small boat.

The Ruby Creek incident is cited frequently by the Sasquatch investigators as strong evidence for their case. Possibly this is because it was the first incident to receive considerable attention since the events in Ape Canyon in 1924. (The Ostman kidnapping story is also from 1924, but it was not disclosed publicly for many years afterwards.) Also the Ruby Creek events happened to be the first ones for years that involved non-Indians, which helped separate it from a context too closely associated, by many, with strictly folklore and myth. The Chapmans were Indian; most of the rest of those who investigated the situation and made sworn statements about it, were not. There had been, as it turned out, dozens of other incidents involving both sightings of the creature and discovery of tracks, in the intervening years–1924-1941. Again, most of these were not disclosed until Dahinden began his investigations, and the reason given by most people for their reticence in coming forward is the usual one–fear of ridicule.

The hundreds of reports that are now on record are there largely through Dahinden's persistent searching. Through publicity surrounding his pursuit have come clues, names, and dates, all of which he has catalogued and searched with the care of a veteran detective on a murder case. And if for a moment we can continue that analogy with policework, it's interesting to speculate on what a court's finding might be, given the mass of circumstantial and physical (footprints) evidence, on the question of the Sasquatch's existence. A court depends on witnesses to a great extent as to what occurred and when; their testimony can bring down a swift decision. Witnesses for the Sasquatch are people such as those so far presented and the ones whose stories still are to come. A court's opinion wouldn't bring us any closer to the creature, nor would it do much to convince the men of science who consider the issue "bosh," that perhaps they are being a bit premature in their judgments. But it might serve to emphasize the point again–that we are dealing with apparently reasonable and credible people as our witnesses.

Joe Gregg was a bus driver with Pacific Stage Lines, out of Vancouver, living near Chilliwack, a few miles south and west of the Harrison-Agassiz area in the Fraser Valley. The story he has to tell is of an incident that happened late at night in November of 1962. It wasn't until five years later that Dahinden heard the story from Gregg, and the man's reasons for waiting that long have a familiar sound:

"I never talked about this for a long time. I figured that if I did, people would recommend that I see a doctor. My wife had been the only one I spoke to about it and she persuaded me to tell some friends the story. (It was through these friends that Dahinden and John Green came to get Gregg's story.)

"When I was talking to (Green), what I had seen and described–and mind you, and I'll swear this under oath, he played recordings of other people's descriptions *after* I had described it–was almost exactly the same as others had seen.

"Anyway, I had been on the Vancouver to Chilliwack late-night run and there were some soldiers who wanted to get back to camp (at the Canadian Armed Forces base near

Chilliwack). They were broke, it was a dirty, wet night and I decided to take them (Gregg was in his car). I drove them to camp and then set out for home. Halfway between Vedder Crossing and Yarrow I saw what I first thought was a very big man with a fur coat on standing on the edge of the road. I slowed down and as I did, this–what I now believe was a Sasquatch–started to lope across the road. I slowed up and followed him with my headlights. I flashed the lights once and he turned my way. His eyes glistened; there was a reflection from them, and the first thing that struck me was that that is an animal characteristic. I'm not a genius by any stretch of the imagination, but I know that this was no human being. He had enormous arms, enormous feet. He was at least seven feet tall and very agile. I would say that he weighed about four hundred and fifty pounds." (The rest of the description of the creature's appearance fits closely the by-now familiar image.)

"He leaped at least six feet up onto a rock on the bank at the roadside. Later, I measured the distance and it was seven feet, ten inches. We also checked later (the next day) for footprints, but the rain had washed away any marks. By the time he jumped I was within fifty feet of him. I know it was dark, and wet. But I saw him.

"For a while, after a couple of friends I later told about it to advised me to stop drinking, I tried to talk myself out of believing what I saw; I thought of all sorts of possibilities of what it might be. But the more I thought this way, the less sense it made. I know what I saw, and no amount of ridicule will make me change my mind. I *know* what I saw."

The Sasquatch is a not uncommon topic of comment and discussion in British Columbia. And as Vancouver is conceded to be the world capital of radio talk-in and hot-line shows, it follows that the Sasquatch is frequently an issue for the airwaves. The programs attract a predictable number of jesters of course, but they also provide an important, anonymous means for those who would otherwise not normally tell of an experience, to do so. It is through this medium that many of the investigators' leads have been started.

One intriguing story–this time not anonymous–was aired on Radio Station CKNW in May of 1969. The host was Jack Webster, a former city editor of the Vancouver *Sun*, and then the acknowledged king of the open-line shows. In the studio were Dahinden, Green, and Jack Wilson, a partner in the Powder Mountain Development Corporation, a company concerned with developing skiing centres. Also there was a veteran Vancouver photographer, John Helcermanas.

According to Wilson, his partner Teddy Osborne had been viewing potential skiing sites on Powder Mountain, about sixty-five miles north of Vancouver and a dozen or so miles in from where Bill Taylor, the highways foreman, saw the creature on the Squamish Highway. Osborne was in a helicopter, flying fairly low, when he saw marks in the snow that puzzled him. He was an experienced bushman but could not recall having ever seen anything resembling what lay below him. He returned and described what he had seen. The following day Wilson and Helcermanas took the helicopter and went to inspect. They found, at a height of 4,800 feet on the mountainside, in a spot where it is quite possible that man has never stepped before, tracks that were fourteen inches long and seven inches wide. (Later photographs of the tracks taken by Helcermanas would be matched against Bigfoot tracks from California and would be found to be almost identical. If we are to keep under consideration the scientists' theory of a gigantic hoax, we should also consider not only the distance from Powder Mountain to northern California (as the crow flies it is something more than seven hundred miles to Sacramento, near where some later sightings occurred), but also the immense problems involved in making a set of tracks along the edge of a glacier, as these were, that run for five miles and offer no evidence on either side of them that would point to their having been manufactured. The idea of a hoax becomes much more unreasonable than the idea of a giant biped on the loose.)

Helcermanas, thoroughly versed in wildlife photography, said he had never been terribly impressed by Sasquatch stories up to this time. "But," he said, "I've never before seen anything like those tracks." The men followed the tracks to the foot of the glacier, a distance of five miles, where the tracks stopped. They concluded that whatever had made the prints had gone into the ice caves which abound there.

The most intriguing aspect of the tracks, apart from the apparently clear evidence that they were made by a biped, was that in each track were husks of balsam buds, and the tracks led from clump to clump of balsam trees.

"I honestly couldn't believe what I was seeing," Wilson said.

The men examined the trees and noted that the balsam buds had been nipped off–not torn, or stripped, but picked–at heights varying between five and six feet. So to this point the debate clearly pointed to some two-legged creature walking through the snow, tramping from balsam tree to balsam tree, picking off buds. There must be another explanation, says Webster, the good journalist concerned with getting both sides of the story, and he then gets the comments of Mr. Al West, a provincial Games Branch regional superintendent. Mr. West's opinion is that the tracks were made by a wolverine bounding across the snow, that each track is actually a front and rear wolverine track combined. He said the balsam seeds were probably blown across the snow and found their natural way into the depressions made by the wolverine. The animal obviously was "on the jump" he explained, and the tracks had been enlarged anyway by the spring melting to two or three times the size they would normally be. He pointed out that debris "is always coming down from the trees," and concluded that "those tracks are not humanoid." A reasonable-sounding argument (though West had not seen the tracks, only the pictures of them) and Wilson listened carefully to it. But then he pointed out that there were no trees on the glacier itself, yet the tracks, containing the debris, went alongside the glacier for some distance. And he reminded the listeners that the debris consisted of only the balsam bud husk, not the whole seed. And besides, he pointed out, the buds were new-growth and one would not expect these to be blown from the trees in any quantity. Wilson repeated the observation made by the two of them on the mountain–that the buds had definitely been plucked from the branches.

The program came to an end when John Green laconically pictured a wolverine repeatedly jumping vertically six feet to pick balsam buds, and Webster added gleefully: "And throwing away the husks!"

Whatever made the tracks on Powder Mountain, according to the three men who studied them and followed them for five miles, it walked on two feet, picked buds and ate the centres before discarding the husks. The image of a hairy biped casually strolling across the snowfields, nipping off snacks from the trees and tossing the remains over its shoulder is almost comic-book material; but it's not as funny as the thought of a wolverine doing the same thing.

Allusions to comical fiction are not uncommon among those who would dismiss the Sasquatch, for whatever reason, as something less than authentic. One such disclaimer is author Odette Tchernine who, in her book *The Yeti*, goes out of her way to relegate the Sasquatch to the level of hokum.

Miss Tchernine in grandly gratuitous fashion says the reports from the Pacific Northwest of North America (there's no evidence that she has ever visited the area or talked to the people involved) remind her of the famous James Thurber cartoon with the caption: "All right, you heard a seal bark!" In her wisdom she explains to her unwitting readers that the Pacific Northwest sightings always come from remote and sparsely populated country. This would come as a surprise to Joe Gregg, whose experience occurred within a short hop of the Trans-Canada Highway which, during its brief run through the Fraser Valley, passes the homes of some 120,000 persons, and is within a thirty-minute drive of the 1,085,000 inhabitants of the Greater Vancouver area–to whom also the news of their isolated condition would be something of a jolt.

The author strongly presses the point of the possibility of a gigantic hoax in North America, but in doing so she fails to consider the incredible obstacles and substantial personal peril implicit in that theory.

Having disposed of the Sasquatch, Miss Tchernine takes a quick look at the Loch Ness monster and she stresses that though it has been the butt of much levity, it has to warrant serious consideration because of the essential integrity of many of those who have reported seeing it, especially the natives of the region. But why a Scottish rustic should be assumed arbitrarily to be more reliable than a Vancouver bus driver or a Ruby Creek housewife, she doesn't explain.

Her book dwells considerably on the Russians' research into their version of the Sasquatch–the Almas–and she relies a great deal on the files of the late Dr. Boris Porshnev, one of Russia's most highly esteemed historians and scientists. Porshnev died in November 1972, a little less than a year after René Dahinden had visited him in Moscow to discuss his studies of sub-human creatures said to live in various parts of the U.S.S.R., especially in the Caucasus and Pamirs.

Porshnev, a department chief in the Institute of History of the Academy of Sciences of the U.S.S.R., was eager to discuss the North American phenomenon with René and was swapping information right up to his death. The following transcript is from a discussion between Dahinden and Porshnev held in Moscow on January 14th, 1972.

All my life, but especially during the last two decades, I have studied the problems of prehistoric archaeology and physical anthropology ... the gathering of the scientific disciplines concerning this field could be the most important in the entire study of the science of man.

One day I was struck by some parallels, some corresponding facts, between my views on the problems of ecology and some other biological aspects, problems that I have studied on Neanderthals, and published data on the Snowman of central Asia. I was struck, so I started to assemble divers data which came from many periods and regions....

I have assembled hundreds of statements concerning these subjects and this has given me, finally, a picture entirely unquestionable on the existence of a being entirely unknown and not scientifically described, but that could serve as one of the greatest discoveries of science in the Twentieth Century.

It concerns the surviving remains of a branch of Neanderthals (in the largest sense of the word) in divers regions of the world, in divers bio-geographic conditions, and the fact that science up to now has not been interested (demonstrating ignorance in my opinion) in the true lines of development of our nearest ancestors.

I am sure that the greatest specialists in the past one hundred years have made discoveries, collected facts and data–really substantial material, especially fossils–and come up with hypotheses and conceptions that were totally false.

Now the time has come to verify and correct these ideas.... I am sure the time has come for the great discussions on the origins of man.

Since 1958 I have participated in searches concerning these beings that we had formerly named "Snowmen." Now we give them several other names. In my scientific work I call them the "relict paleoanthropus." I was with the (1958) expedition organized by the Academy of Science of the U.S.S.R., but this was just the beginning of our researches. The bulk of information was still very scant, very poor.... The leaders of this expedition were not well prepared. The facilities that the academy gave us were not well utilized. All this explains that the expedition was left without much result, it did not answer any of the questions posed.... But at the same time this expedition did give us more knowledge of the local conditions in our mountainous republics in central Asia, of the Caucasus, and other regions where the tales originate concerning these beings. Everywhere, we continue to gather these stories; not only from country people, but also from explorers, from scientists, from intellectuals, who personally have occasionally met these beings....

As for material data, that has remained quite poor up to now. Our attentions formerly were directed to the famous hand of the Monastery of Pang Batch in Nepal (reputed to be that of a Yeti). We have a series of photos which we have studied minutely, getting the point of view of comparative anatomy from professors specializing in these subjects. We have proposed to our colleagues a result quite exact–a conclusion that this hand belongs to a being that is neither monkey nor contemporary man, but of something representing a species very close to contemporary man and maybe a real and true Neanderthal.

Still more data–other prints–were in our possession for a long time, but only in these last few years did we get a chance to study them. (Many earlier Russian scientists pursued the Almas reports but authorities for years refused to make their findings available.) The best imprints here in the U.S.S.R. we have received from the Caucasus, and a few good photos of footprints came from Tien Shan, the mountainous country of central Asia. So now we can compare our findings with those from Canada and the United States.

What (Dahinden) showed us in his photos and his casts (of footprints) is parallel with our findings. We can consider all of these to be truly biological material, truly anatomical, giving substance to a new and much more serious standard of studies and understanding of the hairy beings. (Dahinden's) findings are really very, very important to the scientific point of view. We can study these not only as material for the reconstruction of the feet of the beings, but also for study of its locomotion, the way it moves. And already we have come to important and exact conclusions of these comparative studies.

Those conclusions we look at later.

Apart from the difference in size between the creatures, the Russian data approximates that available on the Sasquatch. The fact that it is somewhat more detailed probably is explained by the extent of the organized research from which it stems–compared with the "unofficial," largely individual pursuits that have compiled the Sasquatch files.

The possibility of a familial bond between the Almas and the Sasquatch, and indeed between any of the similar creatures reported from various parts of the earth, is not at all an unreasonable thought, considering the bridges that once existed between the world's land masses, and especially between Asia and North America. However there is no intent here to claim the Almas and the Sasquatch as twins. Rather the concern is to stress a prominent scientist's (Porshnev's) conviction that his evidence indicates the probable existence of "...the surviving remains of a branch of Neanderthals ... in divers regions of the world..." and his opinion that "...science up to now has not been interested ... in the true lines of development of our nearest ancestors."

That's the message René Dahinden has been delivering to North American men of science for decades.

CHAPTER 4

René Dahinden is the model "man with a mission." If it were not the search for the Sasquatch he was committed to it would undoubtedly be something else with at least as much challenge to it. In a 1967 interview with a Seattle magazine, recalling the first time he heard stories of the Sasquatch, René told the reporter: "Something clicked inside me then and, looking back, it seemed that maybe I'd been searching all my life for a chance like that, a chance to really accomplish something." The words have a familiar ring; they echo those of many a person who started with nothing and pursued a dream.

Few could have started with less than Dahinden. He was born illegitimately on August 23, 1930, in Lucerne, Switzerland. At the age of one month he was placed in a Catholic orphanage and stayed there for a year, at which time, as he says: "Some people came and picked me up, like a dog from a kennel. I was supposed to be adopted, but the legal requirements were never completed. My foster parents were middle-aged and fairly well off. It was a nice enough time, but in 1939 my foster mother died and the man married a younger woman. Neither of them wanted me so I was put into a boys' institution in Lucerne. We went to school and worked on the farm and occasionally we were put out to work for outside farmers. It was a fairly good time."

He had been there a little more than a year when his mother turned up and claimed him. She had married by this time and there was a younger step-brother and step-sister. The arrangement didn't work out. Hardened by the institution experience, René resented anything, real or imagined, that suggested the two younger children were receiving preferential treatment, and he worked out his resentment on them. His home-coming lasted four months, after which it was decided he would be fostered out to a family on a farm.

"That was the beginning of my life. On a farm in Switzerland at that time nothing was as important as the stock; people didn't count for anything. I was five steps lower than a dog. I was fed all right, but I was up before six every morning to clean out the barn and do odd jobs before going to school, and five minutes after I got home I was out in the fields working. That went on for three years solid, no holidays. My places in that house were in the kitchen, up in my room, and outside. In three years I was allowed in the living room once. But you know, later I wrote and thanked those people because from there I went out into the world–when I was about fifteen–and compared with life there, everything I met with was just a joke."

Dahinden took another crack at going "home," stayed two weeks then left, telling his mother he would see her in about three years time. There followed a series of jobs up and down the country–butcher's boy, deckhand, wine bottler, and others–for three years, after which he returned and stayed long enough with his mother to get her to sign the forms needed to get him a passport. Switzerland had become too small.

For the next few years he roamed the length and width of Europe, by bicycle, on foot, and once by rubber dinghy down the River Rhine from its glacier source to Basel. He worked here and there on construction or whatever came along, just long enough to recharge his wallet for the next move, unconsciously pursuing a cause. In Stockholm he met Wanja, the girl who eventually would follow him to Canada and become his wife, and who later would put to him the ultimatum: give up the Sasquatch idea, or give up his family.

Finally, he resolved his general urge to wander into a definite plan to emigrate to Canada. He put in a few hard months labouring, getting himself a stake, and in the last week of October, 1953, sailed from Le Havre to Quebec City. From there he went to Calgary where a farm job awaited him, seventeen miles west of the city on the farm of Wilbur Willick. Perhaps if this farmer Willick had not spent some time during the war years working on the West Coast, Dahinden might not today be immersed in the search for the Sasquatch.

It was just over a month after he arrived, on December 3, that the radio news that night carried a story out of London, England, announcing the formation of the *Daily Mail* expedition to search for the Yeti in the Himalayas. "I heard this," René recalls, "and I said to Willick, 'Now wouldn't that be something; to be on the hunt for that thing?' And he said, 'Hell, you don't have to go that far; they got them things in British Columbia.'"

At first René considered the farmer's response was in way of a put-on at the expense of the new immigrant. But, as he later told the magazine interviewer, something must have clicked, and he kept after his employer to elaborate. Willick could only repeat the odd stories he had heard while working on the coast, the essence of which was that something resembling what the Yeti was supposed to look like populated parts of British Columbia.

The following spring René moved to B.C., finding work in a sawmill at Williams Lake, a town in the Cariboo country, about three hundred highway miles north of Vancouver. He didn't jump immediately into the quest for the Sasquatch, he had the usual concerns of the new Canadian to deal with–adjusting to a new country and its people and language, and making a living among them. "But," he says, "the issue kept floating around in my head." Consequently most of his time during a couple of trips to Vancouver was spent at the museum and the public library, digging up whatever he could on the rumoured creature. The responses he got were far from encouraging. "It's an Indian legend, nothing more," was the general attitude. He persisted though through that year and the next, going deeper into the libraries, both the public and those of the Vancouver newspapers, and by 1956 he had come up with enough material conflicting with the it's-only-a-legend attitude to convince him there was something worth pursuing. He determined to resolve it, hardly realising then that the subject eventually would consume and direct his whole life-style.

His attitude at this stage still was very much that of the high-spirited, energetic young adventurer looking for fun as much as for anything else: "I just thought to myself, 'Hell, it seems as if there's something out there; I'll just go and collect a Sasquatch. Tallyho!' I really wasn't equipped at that time to evaluate what I was reading and hearing. I accepted–probably because I wanted to–the word of those people who said the thing existed and who pointed to stories that had never been investigated." The stories were investigated from then on, and as the findings from them formed a more and more intriguing case for the Sasquatch, so did René's initial carefree and impetuous approach give way to a studied caution and a careful analysis of what he was about.

It was at this time (the summer of 1956) that René first met John Green, and the base was laid for a Sasquatch-seeking partnership that would result in the publishing of Green's two booklets and a great deal of sharing of ideas and theories over a period of some thirteen years until the Bossburg incidents (Chapter 8), when René would begin to view Green's approach as naive, and somewhat selfish, and they would part company.

Green at that time was anything but a proponent of the Sasquatch. He owned and published the weekly Aggasiz-Harrison *Advance* and though well aware of the Sasquatch stories (it was from the Indian language of that region that the word "Sasquatch" was anglicized) he dismissed them as myth. He advised René to forget the whole thing, to go back to his job and leave the Indians to tell their monster stories. But it would be in Harrison, the following year, that René would really swing into the role of Sasquatch hunter that he has maintained since.

In 1957, communities throughout B.C. were frothing over about what to do for a project that would outdo all other communities in celebrating the province's one-hundredth anniversary the following year. Someone on the Harrison village council suggested the Centennial funds be applied to financing a Sasquatch hunt. The council went for it, though not before councillor Robert Gill had objected that: "I don't want people to think I'm a damned fool. I have been here for fifty years and I've never seen such a thing as a Sasquatch. The provincial government won't approve it; they're not such fatheads as that." But the council passed the motion and, recalling Dahinden's persistent presence among them the previous year, invited him back to lead the expedition. Of course they were pursuing a blatant publicity stunt–and it worked. The story was carried world-wide. In Vancouver it bumped news of Princess Margaret's impending visit from the front pages, and Vancouver columnists, and particularly humourists, had a field day. Typical of the response was this column by Eric Nicol in the Vancouver *Province* which followed an offer from an Ontario girl to be Sasquatch bait:

> Call me chicken if you like, but I can't go along with the idea of staking out a beautiful girl to lure a Sasquatch down from the Pitt Lake mountains.
>
> As you've probably heard, a B.C. Centennial committee has set its heart on capturing one of the hairy giants and putting him on display during the '58 celebrations. The Sasquatch will represent British Columbia "Before the Coming of the Safety Razor."
>
> I don't mean that using a girl as bait wouldn't work to catch a Sasquatch. On the contrary, the Sasquatch are notoriously lickerish monsters. Their history is full of abductions of Indian maidens, who were

returned after a year's trial and who subsequently gave birth to a bouncing baby ghoul.

No doubt if you staked a beautiful girl out in those Harrison hills, and sprinkled a spoor of Yardley's Lavender you'd soon have Sasquatch queued up half-way to Princeton.

But presumably there must also be a number of Centennial hunters on the scene, with nets, ropes and rifles. These are the ones I don't trust.

After all, that tangled jungle behind Harrison Lake can do strange things to a white man. And once the Sasquatch scented that there was small print involved in the transaction they would resort to their favourite trick of remaining invisible while throwing stones.

Let's say we have two hunters, Macomber and Flinch, stationed on a tree platform, watching the girl in her comfortably furnished snare in the clearing below. They have been on watch for a week. The weather has turned warm, and the girl reclines decoratively on the ground, sunning in a one-act play suit.

Stretching elaborately, Flinch gets up and prepares to descend the tree ladder.

"Where do you think you're going?" snaps Macomber.

"Time to water the bait," grins Flinch, "I'm off to the old water hole."

"You gave her a drink only an hour ago." Macomber's eyes, reddened from six nights of watching the forest and slightly strabismed from also watching Flinch, glint dangerously. "And every time you come back from the water hole you've got rye on your breath."

"Sulphur, old boy. This Harrison country is lousy with health-giving hot springs." Flinch's grinning face disappears below the platform.

"Hold on, Flinch." Macomber raises himself on

his elbows. "Something else I've noticed. Every time you go to the water hole the Sasquatch start piling rocks into this tree. One of them almost brained me this morning."

"Then keep your head down," yells Flinch, jumping to the ground.

Flinch disappears into the forest. A moment later a large stone crashes through the leaves of the tree, braining Macomber.

Wild and horrible laughter comes from the underbrush. As the girl scrambles to her feet there is a quick movement behind her and a hairy arm seizes her around the waist.

"Please, Mr. Flinch, not so tight," giggles the girl.

In an instant she has been whisked from the clearing. Silence. A figure lies still on the tree platform. And on the edge of the clearing a curiously twisted arm stretches out towards a brown bottle....

Well, as I said, I don't want to spoil anybody's fun. But I feel it's my duty to point out to the Harrison Centennial committee that the Sasquatch plays rough, even by the standards of today's young women.

Instead of using girl-bait, therefore, I suggest they just watch for ads in the paper. They should be able to pick up a Sasquatch at one of those monster sales. No?

And such was the tone of dozens more comments and stories as reporters strove to keep alive what had become an incredibly successful publicity campaign without the instigators so much as putting pen to paper. The general mood of hilarity about the proposed project generated one noteworthy letter to the Harrison council clerk, Paul Trout:

Dear Mr. Trout:

Maybe you white man like Mr. Gill don't believe in Sasquatch but there are lots of things you don't know. Fifteen years ago my old daddy was hurt bad by Sasquatch man he met a mile from Katz. Some white man say my daddy must be drunk when he got his arm broke but no Indians laff. Only whites when they don't know nothing laff like fools.

One thing my daddy was good Catholic and he very little drink likker. White man's poison he say.

What happen he say was daddy was with mama picking berries when he went away from others for rest. He say he only look at trees and sky, then big man over six foot comes running at him from rocks, hit old daddy to ground, hit him on head and side and arm, hit him hard and make grunts. Daddy yell then others come and Sasquatch run away fast. They see Sasquatch running and daddy blood on his head.

Grandma Charlie set bones in arm, she say that little runty Sasquatch maybe other Sasquatch treat him mean so he treat little Indian like old daddy mean.

Grandma say Sasquatch big nice man is catch little Indian woman for make love to all they want. Old daddy scared of woods after, never go anywhere just stay home. He cross river springtime in old boat but never go in trees, maybe mean runty Sasquatch hiding there; hair all over and deerskin. I think maybe daddy drink beer and forget what Sasquatch do but he still good guy, not work but good. He have crooked arm til he die two years ago in 1955.

You white man know lot smart things, smart guys, big car, big house, but you not smart in everything. Maybe Sasquatch hate white man smell and not show. Grandma Charlie say white man smell like old dead men and scare Sasquatch. You maybe see Sasquatch, you go in woods. Catch one if you take Indian (with you). Make Indian go in front with salmon or deer. Leave on tree branch, then catch. Sasquatch eat lots, always want eat. I hope you catch, then you know Indian tell straight. Good luck.

Mary Joe.

One can do little with Mary Joe's letter other than offer

it for consideration. But rather than laughing at the fractured English and Grandma Charlie's racist comments about the malodourous white man, we should remember that even today there are many Indians in B.C.–as well as in the rest of North America–whose first tongue is their native tongue and who have barely a rudimentary control of English. In its own way the letter could be a more than eloquent summation of the whole native attitude to the Sasquatch.

The provincial government ultimately rejected the proposed Harrison project. The council didn't mind; they were already on the map, had had more publicity and good will generated than could have been accomplished with an army of the best PR men. But the council had, unintentionally, served much more than its own interests. Despite the preponderance of humour attached to it, the widespread publicity appears to have been the genesis of the serious consideration that the Sasquatch might indeed be a creature of considerably more substance than myth. When the Centennial ballyhoo had subsided, the information that was to play a major part in shaping René Dahinden's future began trickling in. The Roe story surfaced, followed shortly by the Ostman one and, gradually, others. As the stories were investigated they were made public. René became the source-man for newspaper and radio and TV men anxious to fill their insatiable pages and hours of air-time.

There's no doubt that the growing awareness that some people were taking the phenomenon seriously, encouraged the lunatic fringe to join the act. Sorting out the genuine from the clowns became a large part of the investigators' activities. Nothing that came in could be ignored. Like a good detective the Sasquatch investigator had to follow every lead until he was satisfied that it was based sincerely or otherwise. But apart from the excesses of the fools and hoaxers, the increasing interest served a corollary purpose. As the publicity became more frequent, and its tone less patronizing, those sober and serious individuals who knew well what they had seen were encouraged to say their piece. The open-line radio shows particularly provided the opportunity for those who wished to, to describe their experiences without having to identify themselves to the public and risk ridicule and harassment, at the same time allowing René and his colleagues confidential ("off the air") access to their claims. And it is these that René has been able to pursue in considerable number.

The performance in Harrison in 1957 brought John Green into the picture with René, and that winter René, by now married and the father of a son, moved down to the village and started working for Green on the newspaper. In October of the following year the first stirrings of the Sasquatch in recent times were felt south of the Canadian border.

A bulldozer operator named Jerry Crew, who for several weeks had been finding huge footprints in the soft soil of the logging roads he was building at Bluff Creek in northern California, made a plaster cast of one print and took it to the Humboldt *Times* at Eureka. The photograph of the print and Crew's story hit the wires and interest in Bigfoot was reborn. The footprint that Crew found was indisputably more humanoid than anything else, except that it was sixteen inches long and seven inches wide and was sunk two inches into the road surface where a human foot made an impression only half an inch deep. Crew reported that up to the time he made the cast, he had seen hundreds of similar tracks in the area where he was working–the forests of Weitchpeg, fifty miles north and a little east of Eureka, in the Klamath River country. The logging road was being pushed up the valley of Bluff Creek, a site that later was to take on immense significance for the Sasquatch hunter (Chapter 6). Crew said that neither he nor any of his workmates had ever seen the creature that made the tracks, but that all of them agreed to having had a sense of being watched as they worked in the woods. He speculated that the creature was apparently fascinated by the clearing operations and by the bulldozer, as every day the prints were found in the fresh soil that the machine had moved the day before. Of the tracks he said: "The foot has five stubby toes and the stride averages about fifty inches when he's walking and goes up to ten feet when he's running." Two years before that, stories had come from the woods of heavy logging equipment being tumbled and tossed around by some unknown agent, including the casual scattering of some full, fifty-gallon oil drums.

Crew's story contains what seems to be an inconsistency. Even conceding the hardnosed character generally attributed to loggers and heavy equipment operators, it wouldn't be unreasonable to think that they should have downed tools at the thought of what might be sitting in the bushes overseeing their daily labours. Something that makes tracks of that size, that can apparently fling full fifty-gallon oil drums about, is surely not to be tolerated looking over one's shoulder. But they stayed on the job, with a feeling of being watched. Maybe René has the answer to their behaviour in his theory of what he calls a "psychological safety switch." His reasoning simply is that the Sasquatch concept is beyond man's capacity to accept it, no matter what the circumstantial evidence. He says: "I was down at that same area (Bluff Creek) some years later looking at some fresh tracks. With me was the pilot who flew us down. I asked him if he knew what made those footprints and he said, 'Yes, a Sasquatch.' I asked him if he knew what it looked like and he said, 'Oh, some big hairy thing.' Then I described it to him in detail. He didn't put his shotgun down for three days. But generally people can't accept one hundred per cent what the thing is. Those loggers could look at those prints and conclude that something bloody big and unusual had made them, but their minds couldn't, or wouldn't, take the final step and imagine just what it is. They just let the switch take over that puts the actuality out of reach. If they didn't, they would have been the hell out of there in a short time."

John Green, by now the complete enthusiast, went to

check the Crew story and in his booklet *On The Track of The Sasquatch* he describes how the sheriff at nearby Orleans explained away the tracks (shades of the Verlin Herrington episode in Chapter 2). The upholder of law and protector of the people had discovered that the tracks had been made by a demented (and presumably gigantic) Indian boy who had at one time been kept properly chained up but who had escaped from bondage several years before. There was no suggestion that the sheriff or anyone else had looked for the poor lad before this time. But the sheriff then modified his findings; it was now beyond dispute that the feet that had made the prints were those of a big young man who had been in a correctional camp in the area and had escaped and gone wild. Then he switched again and proved beyond doubt that the tracks were made with false feet that could be bought in any joke shop. There is no record of which of the three theories the sheriff favoured.

One man with whom Green discussed the tracks at Bluff Creek was Bob Titmus, a taxidermist, who from this point would begin to feature frequently in the Sasquatch hunt. At that time, Titmus said that over the years he had had reports from hunters in various parts of the surrounding counties of giant human-like tracks, and that he had always assured them they were seeing bear tracks. It was Jerry Crew who persuaded him to take a look for himself. When he did, though he had no earthly idea what had made the tracks, he was sure it had not been a bear.

Speculation continued over the Bluff Creek tracks, primed at intervals by the finding of a few prints here and there in the neighbourhood, and resulted, in November 1959, in the formation of the first major organized search for the Sasquatch. The Pacific Northwest Expedition was financed by American millionaire Tom Slick, a friend and associate of author Ivan Sanderson who included reports on the Sasquatch up to the early 1960's in his book, *Abominable Snowmen: Legend Come To Life.* Slick had already financed unsuccessful missions to the Himalayas in pursuit of the Yeti.

One result of the Slick expedition, which lasted three years and cost its sponsor untold thousands of dollars, was that René became convinced that no worse possible approach could have been taken in the quest for the Sasquatch. That *Daily Mail* expedition which had first sparked his interest had come to the same conclusion, but probably not for the same reasons; it at least was organized. The Pacific Northwest Expedition evolved as a comedy of errors and malfunctions, any of the several acts of which would have evoked cries of envy from the producers of any of TV's situation-comedy shows. Also, it served to make René for ever after ultra-cautious about the colleagues who ostensibly were as serious as he in investigating the issue: his doubts about his partner John Green, which would climax ten years later, would begin on the Slick expedition. There was money involved, and it would become evident that there were some among the hunters who were determined to find enough continuing "evidence" of their quarry to ensure that the flow of financing would not be interrupted. Perhaps this was done from a strictly mercenary motive; perhaps because those involved were so dedicated to proving the Sasquatch's existence that they would use any means to keep the expedition going until they were proved right and had made their contributions to the theories of evolution. Whatever the motive, the outcome was that the credibility of some became suspect.

Titmus, the taxidermist, was appointed expedition leader, René and others were retained at $350 a month plus living expenses. They were to live in the bush, searching for Bigfoot. There were those among them who had never so much as camped out overnight. After two months René walked out, dismayed by the operation. He returned the following January (1960) but was not destined to stay long. When he came back, Slick had hired Ivan Marx, a professional hunter of mountain lion and bear, as a tracker, and his wife Peggy as cook. Marx is important because of the part he would play later in an even worse fiasco.

Slick apparently was more than a little anxious to be convinced of the Sasquatch's existence. When two men turned up at the base camp one night and spun a tale about having found thousands of tracks, of having smelled the creature and heard it at night, without further investigation he gave them a blank cheque to support their hunt. Within weeks he had to drag the pair into court to prevent further erosion of his bank account. Slick's general approach–signing contracts with all around to cover the eventual capture of the creature, shelling out money to anyone with the flimsiest of claims to knowledge of its whereabouts–created an atmosphere in which the major goal became lost, or at least sacrificed to the potential of the moment. People tended to stir each other up over the promise of things to come; flights of fancy became commonplace and the investigation, the true, skeptical investigation, sank from view. It became a matter of "when we catch it," rather than of "what is there to catch?"

Friction started and grew, especially between René and some of the others as he watched their antics and judged them with his forthright criticism. He drew Titmus's ire especially over one incident. In Titmus's contract with Slick there was a special clause, to the effect that if the Sasquatch was found in one particular area, an extra twenty per cent of whatever finally accrued from the find would go to Titmus. This was because in that area the taxidermist had found an enormous pile of droppings which were assumed to have been deposited by a Sasquatch; assumed, that is, by all except René. During a discussion among Titmus, Slick, and René, Titmus described the find: a massive heap and, above it on a tree trunk at a height of between six and seven feet, grey and brown hairs clinging to the bark where something had leaned or brushed past. René considered the evidence, then brusquely assessed it: "Horse shit." He was not being derisive, rather he was–and correctly as it turned out–reclassifying the droppings, that had grabbed Titmus's imagination and spun him off in a whirl of wishful thinking, as equine. Titmus, René says, has never forgiven him for that incisive description.

On more than one occasion during his association with the Sasquatch search Titmus evolved peculiar notions concerning means of attracting the creature, and this was never better illustrated than during the Slick expedition when he concluded that a sexual lure was required. He assumed the bizarre chore of raiding the women's rest rooms at service stations and retrieving any used sanitary napkins deposited there. The image of him scuttling through dark shadows to skulk at the side of the building, paper bag in hand, waiting for the right moment to dart in and grab his booty, is one to be entertained but briefly, as indeed is that concerning the distribution of his gains: they were nailed to trees surrounding the camp area, in the belief that the quarry would find them irresistible. There was to be no proof that his idea had merit.

Alternative baits were on hand. If the appeal to the Sasquatch libido was to go unanswered, perhaps the avenue to its affections was by way of its stomach. Foodstuffs were planted everywhere, some laid out on trays (presumably with the thought of never underestimating the impact of etiquette), more stuck under bushes, on logs and in trees; everything from sandwiches to fried eggs. And wherever there was bait there was a Brownie box camera pointed at it and attached to a trip-wire to trigger its shutter. There were Brownies dangling from cord, Brownies glued to tree trunks, Brownies jammed in the forks of branches and peeping up from ground-level vantage points, and a veritable tangle of trip-wires all around. Nothing ever developed from the intricate arrangement and René, considering the whole thing silly, removed all the film which happened to fit one of his own cameras and which he felt could be put to much better use out in the field.

His re-allocation of the film went unnoticed by the others, including Green and Titmus who at the time were back in the mountains pursuing signs. While away from the base camp the pair used as a bivouac a large plastic canopy. One day, Green, outfitted in sturdy logger's boots–the ones with spikes all over the soles–walked unthinkingly all over the plastic sheet. The effect of both Green's tramping and René's film removal was felt a year later–still on the PN expedition–when Titmus set off into the bush beyond Bluff Creek on a one-man foray. First, he collected most of the Brownies, neglecting to check the film situation, then he picked up the plastic canopy, all rolled up and ready for him, and off he went. He walked for a day, then made camp. Just as he finished erecting his bivouac the clouds rolled in and delivered a deluge that lasted all night and gave Titmus an unexpected and inescapable shower. He is said to have spent the night laying curses around the absent head of John Green.

René shakes his head and sighs when he recalls the Slick manoeuvres: "There just wasn't much experience among them; it was one thing after another like that. It was a real mess."

It was events in January of 1960 that finally finished René with the Slick expedition, though it would stumble along for another two years on shaky legs. The two men who eventually took Slick for a rough ride on his own chequing account were across the mountains about twenty-five miles from the main camp. With them was Kirk Johnson, a son of one of Slick's business partners. They had hired two donkeys and packed in a mountain of supplies a good day's march from the end of the last access road in the area. From there they would seek Bigfoot. After two days, civilization beckoned to Johnson and one of the other pair and they took off for an evening in Orleans. Their other man became nervous in the late darkness and eventually followed their example, leaving the two donkeys and the several hundreds of dollars worth of supplies and equipment. That night it snowed heavily, completely blocking all the roads leading to the site.

90

Eventually it was decided that René and one other expedition member would go in by helicopter and attempt to bring out the donkeys and the equipment:

"They sent me with this young fellow who had joined the expedition. I never did know what his name was but he had been a sheep-herder in Idaho and was some sort of half-assed poet. He was supposed to be a cook but I never saw him do anything beyond boil water. Anyway, we flew in there and wrapped up as much stuff as the pilot could take aboard in the time he would stay. He was anxious to get out of there because of the weather. He took the most expensive stuff–like all the heaters for example–and left us. There was supposed to be an arrangement whereby a truck would set out and get as far up the road as possible in the next couple of days and we would hike out along the ridge to meet it.

"The two of us stayed there three days eating the best canned ham and drinking whisky and sitting around a big fire. We were giving the truck time to make its way in. One of the donkeys started looking pretty sick so we fed him some whisky and he improved right away.

"When we started the march out we were so confident that the truck would be there (though by now I should have known better) that we took no food with us. What we did have was the last bottle of whisky dangling from one of the donkey's saddle. We didn't even put the saddle on the sick one because this sheep-herder said it had a fever and shouldn't be saddled. He said he was an expert on donkeys. I certainly wasn't, that was the first time ever I had seen one. So we just let it walk along, and lucky we did. We didn't know the trail and this little sick donkey just walked us right out of there. Without him I don't think we would have made it.

"All the way out we were taking sips from the whisky bottle because it was so cold. I began to think the whole thing was funny as hell, but I changed my mind when evening came and we got to the road end and found no truck there. We were getting kind of hungry and the shepherd said if it got any worse we would have to eat one of the donkeys. I told him that if he suggested that again I would have to shoot him. I had the only gun.

"That night we slept in the snow and built a fire round a tree full with pitch. The flames must have been up thirty feet or more. The truck got there the next day and we made it out, donkeys and all.

"But that was the Slick expedition, one insane thing after another. I had to get out of it; I couldn't take any more."

The Pacific Northwest expedition ended abruptly in 1962 when the millionaire's small plane mysteriously disintegrated in mid-flight. All of Slick's records concerning the Sasquatch had been sent to his research institute in San Antonio. This material has never been traced and it has been speculated that Slick's family and/or associates, embarrassed by his participation in the hunt, were quick to get rid of anything smelling of involvement.

CHAPTER 5

René came out of the Slick expedition disillusioned and frustrated. What he had thought was to be a serious search for the elusive thing to which he had permitted himself to become addicted, turned out to be a disorganized gallop through the woods, exploited by opportunists who saw the advantages in playing on the whims of a well-meaning but somewhat impractical millionaire. René went home and put the business behind him while he tried to clarify his thoughts and feelings about where life was taking him. He had been spending increasingly more time in pursuit of the Sasquatch, and less time at home and on the business of providing a life for his wife and son. A boat-rental business he had started in Harrison the previous year (1959) was not going well and casual jobs were not easy to come by. The physical hunt for the Sasquatch, as far as field excursions were concerned, had to be dropped, though the pursuit in the way of checking incidents by letter and telephone as they surfaced, continued. René could not wholly dismiss the problem.

He says: "I had to get less emotional about it. Apart from keeping in touch with people I had to make it just a sideline for a while. I think if I hadn't eased off then I would have gone crazy. I was so wrapped up in it and confused, by the time I left the Slick menagerie, that I was losing sight of everything else."

A number of things occurred in this cooling-off period, a period of almost seven years in which the Sasquatch was pursued by communication only. The boat-rental business had been planned as a means of providing during the summer enough money to finance Sasquatch expeditions during the winter. It didn't work. René is as poor a choice to run a tourist-oriented business as one could find. He is impatient of what he considers to be other people's short-comings; he's abrupt, aggressive, and to some abrasive. He got to the unbusiness-like stage of hoping that each smiling tourist, who looked as though he might want a boat, would change his mind and go away. By the spring of 1962, the rent of the wharf was overdue and René was running into several kinds of friction with the hotel people who had leased it to him. The lease was cancelled and the boat operation sold.

While he was at Harrison however, René had caught onto an ingenious operation which as it turned out was to be the perfect occupation for him. It gave–and still gives–him the opportunity to work at a fairly remunerative job which he can leave at any time he feels it necessary or desirable to do so, for as long as he wishes. One day, watching trap shooters blast at their targets over the waters of Harrison Lake, René noticed that all the shot fell into the shallows. He developed a process for retrieving the spent shot and from there it was a simple development to wash and polish the stuff. The marksmen were delighted to buy it back from him for reloading. He does the same thing now at dry-land gun clubs in the Vancouver area, taking out a contract with the club, and digging up the lead-laden peat and mud and washing out the shot in much the same fashion as the lone prospector washes his gold. He knows how much lead he needs to meet his bills, and is free to chart his own day. Perhaps it was the limited movement he had, as well as the Tom Slick fiasco, that caused René to sit back and review his situation during the early 1960's when, reluctantly, he reassigned the Sasquatch–from passion, to hobby. In retrospect this period becomes comparable to the proverbial lull before the storm.

By 1963, René was spending the summers retrieving shot at the Vancouver Gun Club. Winters were spent in the village of Lumby in the interior of British Columbia, where the Dahindens had bought a house. His second son was born in March of 1963. It was at this time that René again started making tentative forays into the bush, ostensibly regular hunting trips, but all the time with one thing in mind: Sasquatch. He says: "I was realizing again that I wanted to concentrate on nothing else; in fact I simply couldn't think of anything else." By 1965 - 66, the preoccupation was becoming too much for Dahinden's marriage to bear. His trips away from home, collecting information to add to his files, were becoming increasingly longer. "It would have been nice," he says, "if I hadn't had this obsession."

But he did have it, and a man with such an obsession, especially in a small community, stands out. His wife, trying to raise two young children, and working as a school secretary, had to cope with the predictable amount of covert ridicule: "Everytime I was away, she got static and came under pressure from the other women. After all, this thing had dragged on for about twelve years now. I was getting lots of publicity so it was well known what I was doing. And I was beginning to realize that I had to speed the thing up, while my wife was wanting, more and more, security. Also, I was scared stiff of losing my guts, or whatever you want to call it; I was afraid of getting submerged in all the small things people get submerged in. I didn't want any part of the business of just floating along through life, always looking for the easy, safe way out." Also, the several incidents on which he had collected information during those physically slack years, were nudging him back into more direct investigation.

A story that had its origin in 1942 came to the fore in 1965 when the San Francisco *Chronicle* ran the following report. It was told to the *Chronicle*'s George Draper by a Mr. O. R. Edwards and concerned a hunting incident with his partner Bill Cole, and an unidentified creature on Mount Ashland, Oregon.

"We were both moving slowly and quietly round this

patch of brush. Bill went round to the left side; I was on the right.

"I was sweeping the area ahead with my eyes. On one sweep I caught a glimpse of what seemed like an ape-like head sticking out of the brush.

"By the time I had brought my head back to focus on the spot, it was gone.

"Then I heard the 'pad-pad-pad' of running feet and the 'whump' and grunt as two bodies came together.

"Dashing back to the end of the brush, I saw a large man-like creature covered with brown hair. It was about seven feet tall and it was carrying in its arms what seemed like a man.

"I could only see legs and shoes. It was heading straight downhill on the run.

"I was about thirty feet away and the opening in the brush was only ten to fifteen feet wide. At the speed he was going it did not leave me much time to make observations.

"I, of course, did not believe what I had just seen. So I closed my eyes and shook my head to sort of clear things up.

"I looked down the hill again in time to see the back and shoulders and head of a man-like thing covered with brown hair. It was disappearing into the brush some seventy to eighty yards below."

To confirm his recollections of what happened that day, Edwards wrote a letter to Cole (in 1964):

"I guess I should have started looking for you. I don't know why, but I didn't," Edwards wrote. "Maybe I was afraid of the creature. Maybe I was afraid I would find you dead."

Cole replied, acknowledging the incident, but saying, "I don't think he packed me at all. I was conscious all the time. I didn't hurt any place...."

Cole said that after he "quit rolling," he went back up the hill and got his rifle.

"I stood there for some time and looked and listened. I

had a feeling I was being watched and hunted," Cole added.

Edwards mentioned one other thing in his letter to Cole—that for twenty years, "I would not believe what I had seen." And Cole replied to this: "Funny, neither of us had guts to say what happened to us." Before this exchange of letters, Edwards and Cole apparently never discussed what took place on that unusual day.

Edwards also said he saw two more man-animals in the brush at the bottom of the ravine, as he worked his way back to the logging road where their car was parked.

"Then came the damnedest whistling scream that I ever heard, right behind me," he said. "My hackles went up as I whirled just in time to see a flash of something brown disappear behind the tree."

Perhaps the oddest aspect of this remarkable story is that the pair never discussed it together, let alone with others, for more than twenty years. When Edwards did disclose it, it was because he read some of the reports that began to see print in the early 1960's. Had the men been assaulted by a common old bear, the event would have made a magnificent addition to their store of outdoor tales to tell their friends and families. Obviously, each was adequately persuaded that such was not the case. Edwards summed up his feelings about the experience: "There is absolutely no doubt in my mind that they exist, and I know that they are extremely strong and very intelligent."

Stories of actual physical contact with the Sasquatch are in the minority, but Edwards's comment on the creature's strength raises one tale that is simply too good to ignore.

There is no excuse for offering it other than for entertainment and to illustrate the ludicrous extremes to which the Sasquatch theme has been exploited. For the details we have to step forward to June of 1969 and the front page of the *National Bulletin,* where a screaming headline proclaimed: I WAS RAPED BY THE ABOMINABLE SNOWMAN. That surely is the quintessential tabloid headline; the deskman responsible for it probably covered his typewriter and retired forthwith, his career pinnacle truly scaled.

The story came at a time when the scientific world, or at least some of its members, were agog at the alleged existence of a sub-human specimen, apparently dead of bullet wounds in the head, encased in a block of ice and "owned" by Frank D. Hanson, a Minnesota showman. I'm not about to tread the convoluted trail of the Iceman story. Sufficient to say that a number of prominent scientists were for a while conned into believing it, that the FBI became involved, and that now the experts tend to regard it as a very clever send-up.

In 1969, however, it was hot stuff and it seems that tenders were out for details of how it was killed. The *Bulletin* won hands down in my opinion. The story was told by one Helen Westring who, at the time of the deed, had been hunting, alone, in the woods near Bemidji, Minnesota, when she met an "Abominable Snowman." The description was standard for the Sasquatch, except for the eyes, which were pink and fringed with white hair, and the behaviour which was quite out of character according to all our records. The great beast set to and tore off Miss Westring's clothes, "like one would peel a banana." The foreplay over with, it spent a few preparatory seconds staring at her, with particular concern for "the area between my legs," then, demonstrating a singular lack of gallantry, it dumped her on her back among the leaves and, with what for an Abominable Snowman would seem to be a suitable degree of snorting and heaving, had its way. Fortunately, Helen fainted and was "out" during most of the carryings on. When she did regain her senses she had enough of them to permit her to grab her gun and shoot the creature– dead in the right eye, where the Iceman's fatal wound was said to be.

That's *one* story of how the Iceman was sent to its frosty tomb. There are others, but they would be anticlimactic.

The fact that the Sasquatch phenomenon has been able

to survive such treatment as Helen's story is remarkable testimony to its endurance, if to nothing else.

But to return to the period we were considering–the quiet years, when the cataloguing of information supplanted the active search. In the San Francisco *Chronicle* story, Mr. Cole remarked on the feeling he had of being watched and hunted. The same eerie feeling was noted by a number of those in the search party that looked for Jim Carter, the skier who vanished on Mt. St. Helens (Chapter 1), and it has occurred on many other occasions.

On Labour Day weekend in 1959, a Mr. and Mrs. Bellvue were camped at Hidden Lake, a few miles from the town of Enderby in B.C.'s Okanagan Valley. They had been there for five days, relaxing and fishing. Mrs. Bellvue left the tent area and went off to collect some camp fire kindling. It was about 7.30 p.m., before the onset of dusk. She had been busy for only a few minutes when suddenly she became intensely aware that she was being watched. She looked up, and off to one side, to a small knoll and a pine tree about fifty feet away. Beside the tree, and partly concealed by its lower branches, stood a tall, heavy, human-like figure. It was bulkier than any man she had ever seen and appeared to be "well over six feet." It was covered with rust-coloured hair which lightened around the chest area. The forehead sloped back, parts of the face were without hair, the nose was "just a flat area with two holes," and the mouth appeared to be little more than a slit. The creature was motionless, studying her.

"I felt that it didn't want me to know it was there," she recalled. It remained still, watching her, and slowly she backed away from the spot and returned to the campsite. She was bewildered. Had she really seen what she thought she had seen, or was her mind tricking her? If indeed she had seen properly, what in God's name was it? Trying to sort out her thoughts, for a while she said nothing to her husband. "I thought he would think I had lost my marbles." The pair went to bed. "I was trying to get to sleep," Mrs.

Bellvue says, "when all of a sudden I knew we had to get out of there. That's when I told him about it." Mr. Bellvue did not show the surprise his wife expected. Although he had seen nothing, as he told René several years later (when the story came to light following a radio talk-show): "The night before, I'd been fixing my fishing tackle when suddenly something told me it was okay to spend that night there, but we'd better leave tomorrow. I can't explain it; the thing just came into my mind. I hadn't been thinking about anything but fishing. I wasn't afraid, just uneasy all the time afterwards."

His wife's story was enough to confirm his feelings. They began striking camp and loading their gear. As Mr. Bellvue dismantled the last tent pole, husband and wife heard the sound of running feet, moving gradually away from them through the bush. The sounds faded and disappeared. The Bellvues packed up and left.

"I keep thinking about it," Mrs. Bellvue says in recalling the incident. "I know I was tired at the time, and that's when a person's mind can play tricks; but there the thing was, and it was what you call a Sasquatch. There's nothing else it could have been."

Another Okanagan woman, a Mrs. Calhoun from Penticton, had a more direct experience with a similar creature three years later, but 250 miles further north in B.C., just off the Cariboo Highway between Quesnel and Prince George. Mrs. Calhoun, apparently an experienced outdoorswoman, was on a prospecting and fishing holiday with her daughter in late August of 1962. She was armed with a hunting rifle and was on the bank of a small creek, about one o'clock in the afternoon, when she turned to greet–as she thought–her daughter who had gone to bring the lunch. No more than ten yards from her stood a creature whose appearance caused her to swing up the rifle and take steady aim at the middle of its head.

"My first, fleeting impression was that it was a human with very long arms," she said, when René tracked her down several years later. "But it took me weeks to get out of my mind the look it was giving me from its small, black eyes as it stood there. It was like an ape–but like a human as well. It had blond-brown hair on its chest and long, loose, matted hair on its head. It had high cheek bones, a wide, flat nose, a forehead that sloped back, and a mouth that stuck out. It opened its mouth, but didn't make a sound; just stood there looking at me. I started moving away and the thing jumped into the bush and disappeared. All the time as I was backing off down the creek, I knew I was being watched." Then Mrs. Calhoun recalled a further detail about the creature–it had something around its waist, animal skin or garment she couldn't recall. Nor was there any indication whether the waist-piece was meant to serve modesty or utility.

In René's files there are two reports of unusual creatures wearing a sort of breech clout–Mrs. Calhoun's, and one dating back to 1947 and involving Mrs. Nellie Werner and her husband. In each case the creatures apparently did not have a full covering of body hair, but did have noticeably long hair on their heads. The Werner episode took place on a logging road on Grouse Mountain in North Vancouver, a spot only ten to fifteen minutes car journey from downtown Vancouver. The Werners were driving in a jeep when, rounding a bend in the logging road, they almost ran into two beings that they concluded were not quite human. They were naked "except for a skin wrapped round them." Both had bare feet (no mention of hair on the feet or body) and long hair down to their shoulders. One had (and this is unique to the Sasquatch files) a stick over one shoulder with what may have been a bag of sorts tied to the end of it, and he seemed to be leading the other who, the Werners thought, possibly had his hands tied together. Both the creatures had "huge" feet. The one with the stick was around eight feet tall, the other one about six feet. They had heavy, bushy eyebrows over very small eyes, and flat, wide noses. The smaller of the two was very broad throughout the body, but the bigger one tapered down from the shoulders and was "quite slim." The Werners, relating the story almost twenty years after the event, said they had never heard the word Sasquatch until several years after their experience. They felt that what they had seen was vaguely some sort of wild man.

Maybe they were pretty close, at that. Whatever the purpose might have been of the breech clouts mentioned in the Calhoun and the Werner stories, the implication is that some level of intelligence was at work in their use–a cause and effect thought process that one would usually associate with human thinking rather than with animal behaviour. And the fact that one carried a stick with something attached to it, and that the smaller of the two was apparently being led "with its hands tied," tends to advance the speculation of an intelligence at work. The Werners noted that the taller of the pair was "slim." This is not a common element in the Sasquatch history, where most of the reports concern an immense bulk–but neither is it unique. Joe Gregg, the bus driver whose experience was related in Chapter 3, remarked on the particular "agility" (not just speed) of the creature he saw. His description was of something at least seven feet tall with a weight of about 450 pounds. This would present a creature somewhat more slender than the ones estimated at twice that weight but of the same height. And in May of 1956, Stan Hunt, an auctioneer from the small Okanagan town of Vernon, reported that he had seen two unidentifiable creatures near the village of Flood, which is across the river from Ruby Creek, where Jeannie Chapman and her children fled in fear from their home. Hunt said a "seven-foot man covered with grey hair," ran across the road in front of his car, while a similar creature, "gangly, not stocky like a bear," stood in the bush beside the road.

So with the suggestion of a functioning intelligence, and the presence of apparently human-like proportions, there appears ground for an area of speculation that may or may not upset the protectors of orthodox anthropology–that is, the possibility of productive mating between humans and the creature we call the Sasquatch, with the result: a being possessing some of the characteristics of each, ratios uncertain.

Albert Ostman, the logger "kidnapped" by the Sasquatch, was, in the later interviews with him, quite firm about his notion that the family had him marked as a source of progeny. And there is another graphically documented source to which we can turn for a foundation for the mixed-mating speculation, although again we have to leave North America and consider more of the research of the Russian, Boris Porshnev.

The story is that of a Neanderthal-type female named Zana who, records show, died in the late 1800's in a small village near the town of Ochamchire on the Black Sea. Porshnev pursued her story, talking with old people in the village who clearly remembered Zana, several of whom attended her funeral. Zana was captured when quite young by a band of hunters. She was passed or sold to a number of owners, finally ending up as a gift to the well-to-do Genaba family. At first she was kept chained and firmly enclosed, but as she became accustomed to her human surroundings she was permitted to move about freely. Zana could not "speak" as such, but she did make sounds that carried their intent, at least as far as the village children and dogs were concerned, whose attempts to torment her she quickly terminated–but she was capable of understanding and following orders given by her owner. She was tall, bulky, and her dark skin was covered with reddish brown hair. Her face was broad, with prominent, high cheek bones, a very flat nose, and small eyes which in some lights appeared red. She had immense physical powers, reportedly being able to out-run a horse easily and to swim comfortably through the most turbulent of waters. It seems odd that she did not apply her strength and speed to escaping, but she apparently became content to live among humans, performing simple tasks such as grinding grain and collecting wood for the fires. Perhaps it was the consideration that being provided for was an improvement over living off the land which made her happy with her lot; or maybe it was the fact that her owners introduced her to and kept her supplied with wine–to which she is said to have become very partial, drinking great drafts of it and then curling up happily in a ball and sleeping for hours.

Whatever the reason, she stayed. And–and there seems little doubt about the truth of this according to Porshnev's findings–she became the mother of a number of children by several human fathers. Her first confinements were successfully concluded without assistance, but the children died, apparently through Zana's well-meaning but primitive method of cleansing them–she plunged them into the icy water of the river. After that four more children were born and, due to the intervention of villagers, survived. The youngest, a son named Khvit, died in 1954, aged about seventy. All of these four, who were said to possess more or less normal human faculties, had children and they are now living in various parts of the small Caucasus republic of Abkhaz.

Porshnev talked with people who had worked with Khvit before he died. They recalled his dark skin, his immense physical strength, and his short temper. He would fiight at a moment's provocation, and rarely lost. They remembered also his unusually high-pitched voice and his admirable talents as a singer. Then, in 1964, Porshnev met Khvit's son and daughter, born of his second marriage, in the coal town of Tkvarcheli where both worked in the mines. Both children had inherited their father's looks, particularly his dark colouring, which was unusual enough in that town to be remarkable. Like his father, the son was noted for his uncommon physical strength and for the extensive range of his high-pitched voice, with which he was adept at imitating animal calls.

Porshnev's intention was to unearth the skeleton of Zana.

It's interesting to note that she was buried in the Genaba family cemetery, especially in light of the ubiquitous belief that some of her children were fathered by Edgi Genaba, the head of the family. When Khvit died he was buried beside his mother. Porshnev did not obtain the skeleton and was still making efforts to do so when he died.

There is at first thought a slight conflict between the Zana story and our speculation on mixed-mating in the Pacific Northwest. Zana's offspring were predominantly human; the slimmer creatures sighted here appear to have had more "creature" characteristics. Possibly this can be accounted for by some radical biological difference between the Almas and the Sasquatch (as we stressed earlier, there is no claim that the two are identical). Possibly Zana herself was the result of a mixed-mating and genetics determined the peculiar development of her children. I do not pretend to qualifications that would permit me to pursue these implications further; the question is one for students of genetics, should any ever get around to considering it.

There are two more incidents to be considered of those that came to light during the years when René was taking a breather. Both happened in 1966 and undoubtedly played an important part in his decision to resume the search. The events occurred within sixty miles of each other and had one curious element in common—the creature involved was covered with white or silver hair.

About 11 p.m. on September 19, a young man from Yakima, Washington, Ken Pettijohn, was driving back to the town after having taken a friend, who was on leave from the army, home, about ten miles west of Yakima. There was a rain and lightning storm in progress. Suddenly Ken slammed on his brakes, the car skidded wildly, the engine stalled, and the car stopped, its lights illuminating a creature which Ken estimated at about seven feet tall and "very heavy." It was only feet from the car, and its greyish white covering of hair was clearly visible in the headlights, as were its flat nose and thin lips, and its "red eyes—like a rabbit's." It showed no fear–rather a good deal of curiosity with this machine that had almost run it down. It lifted one arm, as though to shield its eyes from the lights. Then it inspected the car and its occupant. It walked all around the car, taking little more than one stride from front to rear, then bent down for a closer look at the driver, who noted later: "It wasn't frightened, and it wasn't aggressive." Ken re-started the motor and accelerated down the highway. "The last I saw of it was through the rear-view mirror," he said. "It was standing in the road with the lightning flashing around it, watching me leave." Pressed to elaborate on the colour of its eyes, he said, with what appears sound reasoning, "I wasn't concentrating on staring him in the face." Ken returned to the spot the next day, with friends, and found several human-like footprints on the road shoulders.

The other situation involving a "white" man-animal contains some remarkable testimony. A group of youths from Richland, Washington, about sixty miles from Yakima, claim to have met on several occasions during 1966, at close range, with what they called the "white demon." Not only did they see it, they also charged it with a car and used both a rifle and a shotgun on it. One of the youths, Greg Pointer, who insisted he would take a lie-detector test at any time on the subject, said the creature was seen frequently in the area of some old gravel pits outside the town. He described it as "whitish-grey, about eight feet tall and a minimum of six hundred pounds, with red eyes. It had a flat face and it walked like a human." Another of the boys, Roger True, said he used a .270 calibre rifle on it at a range of only twenty feet, hitting it "at least three times," but not knocking it down. And a third member of the group, Tom Thompson, blasted at it with a 12-gauge shotgun from only ten yards. "It screamed, a sort of high-pitched squeal, but the shots didn't stop it from running away," he said. Greg Pointer described how one group, after throwing rocks at the creature for a while, then boarded their car and tried to ram it. It scraped one hand down the side of the car as it passed, but this was the only gesture of retaliation, or aggression in any form, that it made during all the attacks levelled against it.

The youngsters were asked to go over their story repeatedly and they did so, insisting that they were guilty neither of fabrication nor exaggeration. They pointed out that they had on more than one occasion reported the incidents to both police and their parents, neither of whom had taken them seriously.

The colouring of the Yakima and Richland visitor(s)–we could be dealing with the same creature in each instance–can be considered from two viewpoints. First, we could be dealing with an albino. This could account for the physical appearance–whitish with red eyes–and possibly for the unusual behaviour, that is the excessive curiosity and the apparent inclination to get closer to humans. In any species "freaks"–and an albino is such–are generally shunned if not actually driven out. They tend to develop habits and attitudes different from their peers, to accommodate and /or compensate for their special status. That could well be the case here–provided we accept the stories. On the other hand the explanation might lie in age, even senility. The Russian research indicates that the sub-humans of their studies follow in their development many of the patterns of man, including the process whereby the hair turns grey or white with age. If we take that line then maybe the peculiar behaviour of these two creatures can be attributed to the weight of years and the changes that often accompany it.

Whatever the case may be, it was such happenings that by the beginning of 1967 provided René with the fuel to take up the hunt again. John Green was ready for more also, so the decision was made to take a trip through the northwest of the U.S., renewing old contacts and making new ones, generally consolidating their knowledge of the events of the past several years and using them as a basis for a renewed, all-out pursuit of the Sasquatch. René explained to his wife that it was now all or nothing; she either supported him in his beliefs, or she didn't. By the spring of that year she had decided also–René was to choose between his obsession with the Sasquatch and his place with the family. Fourteen years of delving and questioning and wondering had caught up with him, and their aggregate effect was stronger than anything else. The result was a separation and subsequently a divorce.

There was something almost omen-like about the time chosen for the break. Events in the fall of 1967 were to open up the Sasquatch issue to an extent that it had never known before. And those events would set the scene for happenings within the next two years that became stranger and stranger.

CHAPTER 6

René refers to 1967 as "the big year."

On Monday, August 28, he took a phone call from John Green. Green was just back from a trip to northern California to look at tracks which had turned out to be too old and crumbled to serve any useful purpose. Now he told René that hundreds of new tracks had been reported in the Bluff Creek area, near the summit of the five-thousand-foot Blue Creek Mountain.

It was essential to move immediately in order both to examine and protect the tracks before the news leaked too far and drew the heavy-footed public. Green was able–to the surprise of both–to persuade the Vancouver *Sun* to put up five hundred dollars for a charter plane and the pair, along with dog handler Dale Moffitt and one of his tracking dogs, flew to the air strip at Orleans, near Bluff Creek, arriving at the tracks site after dark.

The tracks had been discovered when a member of a work crew had investigated the disturbance of a stack of tractor parts that had been left on the side of the road. The heavy pieces had been strewn about in the bush and the area was surrounded by huge footprints.

The hunters made camp at nearby Onion Lake, then examined as much as they could of the tracks using flashlights. The dog was anxious to get on the trail of whatever had made the tracks, but the hunters, weighing the wisdom of plunging into the bush in the dark supported only by the glow of flashlights, opted for caution, and daylight.

In the morning, the men counted more than a thousand footprints and they were the clearest any of them had ever seen. They appeared to have been made just after a brief rain had dampened the top layer of dust. The detail was so fine that the surface lines of the skin on the bottom of the foot were detectable. Also, the prints belonged to three different pairs of feet clearly distinguished by size. The tracking dog was let go on the spoor, but, with the temperature hovering around the 100° mark, turned up nothing. Meanwhile the group was awaiting the arrival of Don Abbott, the anthropologist from the British Columbia provincial museum, whose superiors had condescended to his making the trip after listening to descriptions of the number and condition of the footprints. This was the first time on record that any authoritative institution had become formally engaged in Sasquatch activity. (It was his involvement in this episode that prompted Abbott to write the form letter with which we opened Chapter 2.)

While they waited, news of the tracks spread, and soon carloads of curious local people were at the scene. Most of them drove over the tracks before they saw them, destroying many. The ones who didn't wheel over them raised dust clouds which settled back into the prints and obscured much of the finer detail. The hunters preserved as many as they were able to. At the same time, word came of more tracks that had been found a couple of miles away and two thousand feet down the mountain. These, deeply impressed, stretched along a sandbank in Bluff Creek, but by the time René and company got to them they had been largely destroyed by a group of loggers who had found great diversion by stomping in and around the footprints, comparing the sizes with their own booted feet. The frustrations inherent in incidents such as these are obvious when we remember that for René the footprints are the firm physical evidence on which he lays much of his argument.

Don Abbott finally arrived on the Thursday, by which time the tracks were more than three days old. He came with a new method of "lifting" the prints. Up to now the accepted practice had been to pour in liquid plaster and lift out the mould when it hardened. The new plan was to prepare the ground around the print with a strong fixative and then lift the piece out complete, so that the actual footprint, rather than a model of it, could be available for study. Abbott was sufficiently impressed by what he saw to call zoologists at Humboldt University, the nearest source of such specialists. It took a considerable effort on his part to convince them that they should at least take a look. They waited until the following Friday to make the trip, and the delay was unfortunate. In the interval most of the remaining tracks, including the ones Abbott had prepared for lifting, were scraped away by an enthusiastic grader operator who liked nothing better than a smooth logging road in his wake. The Humboldt scientists went away unimpressed.

Looking back at this Bluff Creek episode, René acknowledges the mistakes. Instead of settling down to a serious analysis of the tracks, they were consumed by the notion of capturing whatever had left them. "We were still at that time hoping to walk right up on its tail and grab it," he says. From that time he became concerned more with establishing the authenticity–or otherwise–of footprints than with apprehending their originator. If he could produce evidence strong enough to convince the skeptics of science that here was something they had better take a second look at, he would score vital points. His realignment of priorities as we shall see was not always subscribed to by his colleagues.

The party left Bluff Creek. If they had known what was scheduled to take place there in a few weeks time, they undoubtedly would have battened down their tents and sat tight. The incident, which was to bring René back at a fast run, remains the most controversial element in the Sasquatch files.

But that was in the future. René and John Green returned to Vancouver, Abbott to Victoria with a report for his bosses at the museum. Three weeks passed before any of the information was released to the newspapers, three

111

weeks in which the museum's senior men did their best to persuade Abbott that the situation merited no serious consideration. When René and John Green eventually were invited to Victoria to meet with the museum brass, Abbott told René: "I don't even know any more if there were footprints there because they insist there couldn't have been!"

René was nursing the hope that out of the meeting might come something in the way of support for further research into the Sasquatch question. He might have known better. In the meeting, which lasted three hours, he and Green faced B.C.'s Minister of Recreation and Conservation, Kenneth Kiernan, museum director Dr. Clifford Carl, (deceased) and the museum's mammal expert, Charles Guiget. During the three hours, the government men did their best to discredit everything René had achieved. Finally, exasperated by their hedging and circumlocution, René said: "I'm sick of your scientific jargon. The question here is not are there or are there not Sasquatches, it is–who, or what, made those damned tracks?" He suggested the government finance a proper investigation, pointing out that if nothing else came of it, the government would reap immense publicity which might well be reflected in increases in the tourist industry.

"We want the most skeptical, the most cynical experts to be ready to move when the next tracks are found," he told them. "But we want them to have an open mind, because either those footprints are faked–in which case we have no Sasquatch–or they are real–in which case we sure as hell have something!" He suggested that if the government cared to employ him and Green on the project, that would be quite in line because: "You employ enough deadheads as it is; two more wouldn't sink the boat." The government men laughed, but it's debatable whether they were amused. The minister kept passing the ball to Guiget, who advised René that if he had bothered to follow the Bluff Creek tracks properly he would have found that they ended back at the road.

"–And jumped into a car and drove off, no doubt," René concluded for him. Guiget affirmed that that indeed was his belief. Guiget's unshakeable attitude–one to which René has become well accustomed–was: there isn't the remotest chance of there being anything out there because we (game department zoologists and biologists) have never seen it. It was obvious there would be no further help coming from the B.C. government.

The Vancouver newspapers and the other sources he tried in the city offered nothing beyond encouraging noises of the let-us-know-when-you-get-something kind. To René this was simply more of the same old story. He had hoped that the description of the tracks on Blue Creek Mountain would have shaken open some of the closed minds. When it didn't, he shrugged it off and turned elsewhere. Armed with his stacks of research notes, he headed south for San Francisco to present his case to the newspapers there, with the *Chronicle* especially in mind.

While he was riding the bus down through Washington and Oregon, a former rodeo cowboy from Yakima, Roger Patterson, was on his way in to the Bluff Creek area where, on October 20, he would shoot twenty-four feet of 16mm colour movie film of what he claimed was a female Sasquatch. The authenticity of that film still is unresolved, although the opinions of those qualified to judge and who still are assessing the film, including British and Russian analysts, leans more and more to the positive.

Roger Patterson had followed the Sasquatch phenomenon for several years and in 1966 had published a small, flamboyant paperback book called *Do Abominable Snowmen of America Really Exist?* It is studded with exclamatory sentences and would-you-believe statements, and is really little more than an anthology of newspaper clippings laced together with Patterson's circus-poster style prose. This, and the fact that Patterson was a Sasquatch buff, was enough for the cynics, who immediately dismissed the film as a hoax or–though they were careful not to say so on the record–a deliberate fraud aimed at cashing in on the subject. Their reasoning, that the sighting of a Sasquatch by anyone linked with the search for the creature must be automatically suspect, is not easy to accept. It rings of the shallowest sort of cynicism and raises doubts about their capacity to analyse. Some of those who rejected the film most firmly never even saw it. And their instant expertise has never been justified.

But to return to the event:

Patterson and a partner, Bob Gimlin, had ridden into the Bluff Creek area on saddle horses, continuing the searching that Patterson had pursued intermittently for about six years. They were in rugged country, twenty-five miles from the nearest blacktop. Coming round a sharp bend in the creek, the horses suddenly reared, startling both men. Patterson's horse fell and as it did he saw the cause of the animals' alarm, across the creek about ninety feet distant: a large creature meeting all the qualifications of the Sasquatch. At the same moment he saw it, Patterson grabbed his movie camera, already loaded, and started running towards the creature, filming as he went. One result of this naturally is an unevenness in much of the film. However, to what Patterson and Gimlin saw: it was a human-like creature. Later they estimated its height at close to seven feet, and from impressions left on the sandbar they guessed its weight at about 350 pounds. She–there are pendulous breasts clearly visible in the film–was covered with short, shiny black hair. On her head the hair came down to past where the eyebrows would be, and it was up to her cheekbones on the face. On the back of her head was a kind of peak, but Patterson could not tell whether this was a bone formation or some sort of hair ridge. There was no neck visible, rather the bottom of the head appeared to become part of the heavy back and shoulder muscles. The muscles of the buttocks were distinct, and the creature walked with a human-like gracefulness, swinging its arms.

Patterson was tumbling and running after the creature,

114

trying at the same time to focus his camera, when suddenly, as if to spare him further trouble, she turned to face him, apparently not frightened by his nearness. (Considering the relative physical sizes–Patterson was a small man–this perhaps is not surprising. He was not carrying a gun and it has been speculated that the creature was aware of that, otherwise it would not have turned so casually.) While Patterson was shooting his movie footage, Gimlin was trying to control the panicked horses. It's interesting to consider what had made them so twitchy; was it simply the sight of the thing? Or was it the smell? Several of the incidents in the Sasquatch files include reports of a foul smell associated with the creature (as do descriptions of the Russian Almas); a smell that has frequently turned usually aggressive hunting dogs into whimpering, hysterical cowards. Both Patterson and Gimlin reported a strong, offensive odour at the time.

The Sasquatch did not stare for long at Patterson. By the time Gimlin had contained his horse and had ridden across the creek, the lady of the woods had made off into the deeper forest. During her casual ambling along the creek bank her measured pace was between fifty-four and fifty-six inches.

Patterson and Gimlin, understandably excited, followed the creature's tracks until they cut off along a tributary, at which point they allowed caution to temper the pursuit. They were afraid the creature, if further harassed, might turn on them. The pair turned back and headed for Eureka, with the intention first of getting the film in for processing and then of getting scientists to the scene.

They called Don Abbott and asked that he get down there and if possible to bring tracking dogs. It was natural that Abbott should be their first consideration since he was to this point the only scientist of any stature to have demonstrated a serious interest in the question. However, Abbott declined, suggesting that the film when processed could be studied at leisure.

René arrived at Willow Creek the day after the filming.

Patterson and Gimlin had returned to the film site and covered some of the tracks preparatory to casting them, and had cast one. It rained heavily that night and the creek rose quickly. Aware of the dangers–two years earlier there had been massive floods which had washed out whole sides of the hill–Patterson and Gimlin had not stayed long. As it was, they had a hair-raising trip out, their truck on several occasions coming frighteningly close to sliding off the narrow muddy road on Onion Mountain.

Patterson had released the story in Eureka and the wire services had done their job. There were phone calls from across the world, asking for confirmation and elaboration. The film was being processed and Patterson, as he told René, didn't know whether he had anything that would stand up.

Next day, the group viewed the film at the Yakima home of Patterson's brother-in-law. René says, "I knew what I was going to see, I'd had the thing described often enough, but it still gave me a hell of a shock when I saw it. Your first reaction is, 'Ah, comeon...' you know, looking for the zipper in the fur suit. But then you start looking at it one thing at a time...." They watched it until their eyes blurred, firing questions the whole time at Patterson. Finally, with only slight reservations–born no doubt of years of investigating fools and false alarms–they agreed that they had a Sasquatch on film.

Patterson's first impulse was to rush off with the film to New York and stun the world of science, at the same time building dreams of making a vast fortune. René and Green however, more familiar with the attitudes they knew he would face, argued against the move. "Go to New York," René told him, "and they'll laugh you out of town. You'll be considered only a freak with a monster movie." The warning was to prove more accurate than René probably knew.

Patterson thought exclusively in terms of instant bigtime. "With him it had to be a million bucks or nothing,"

René says. Between them though René and Green persuaded Patterson to stay on home ground, for the time being. Patterson agreed to take the film up to Vancouver, where at least there was familiarity with the Sasquatch and where it was conceded that René and Green were serious researchers. Showings of the film were arranged for scientists and reporters at the University of British Columbia and in a Vancouver hotel. The film was run several times, both straight through and in stop-frame sequence.

Both Vancouver newspapers, the morning *Province* and the afternoon *Sun,* ran the story at the top of page one the next day. In each story there was a remarkable scarcity of the comic tone that had always previously characterized Sasquatch material. Tony Eberts of the *Province,* that paper's unofficial Sasquatch writer, best summarized the responses to the film:

> The legend of the Sasquatch took a giant hairy step closer to reality Thursday night.
>
> A group of B.C.'s leading zoologists and anthropologists examined a movie film purporting to show a female Sasquatch...and not one scientist called it a hoax.
>
> The film (shows)...a huge hair-covered animal that looks like a cross between a gorilla and Mae West.
>
> Dr. Ian McTaggart-Cowan, dean of graduate studies at UBC and the province's leading zoologist, summed up the more cautious opinions when he said: "The more a thing deviates from the known, the better the proof of its existence must be."
>
> But Don Abbott...spoke for the dozen or more scientists who appeared remarkably close to being convinced:
>
> "It is about as hard to believe the film is faked as it is to admit that such a creature really lives. If there's a chance to follow up scientifically, my curiosity is built to the point where I'd want to go along with it. Like

most scientists however I'm not ready to put my reputation on the line until something concrete shows up—something like bones or a skull."

Frank Beebe, well-known Victoria naturalist and provincial museum illustrator, commented: "I'm not convinced, but I think the film is genuine. And if I were out in the mountains and I saw a thing like this one, I wouldn't shoot it. I'd be too afraid of how human it would look under the fur.

"From a scientific standpoint, one of the hardest facts to go against is that there is no evidence anywhere in the western hemisphere of primate evolution–and the creature in the film is definitely a primate."

One objection frequently raised in the Sasquatch argument is the question of the lack of relics such as bones and skulls, and it was raised again in February of 1968 when Dr. Clifford Carl, the B.C. museum director, wrote a summary of the official attitude to the Patterson film and other evidence collected to that time. He said: "Scientists and laymen who have studied the Sasquatch film and other evidence are faced with two improbabilities. If the tracks, sightings and photographic evidence are not real the Sasquatch is a hoax of colossal magnitude. If the evidence is real, the second improbability, that a pre-historic man-type mammal has been with us without leaving concrete evidence (teeth, bones, etc), is staggering to the scientific world."

Later we examine formal scientific opinions on the Patterson film particularly and on the Sasquatch generally, but it is timely to offer some explanation for this particular question of physical remains. First, if this creature exists as it is described, possessing evidently some human or near-human attributes, it should not be unreasonable to consider that it would be capable of secreting the remains of its dead in a manner, and a location, that would preclude their being discovered. We must remember the vast extent of its presumed habitat and the degree of inaccessibility to man of much of it. Another explanation, a somewhat simpler one, was suggested by author-scientist Ivan Sanderson who, in writing about the Patterson film in *Argosy* magazine in February 1968, said: "...ask any game warden, real woodsman or professional animal collector if he has ever found the dead body or even a bone of *any* wild animal–except along roads of course, or if killed by man. I never have, in forty years on five continents! ...Nature takes care of its own, and damned fast, too...."

The consensus following the Vancouver showing of the film was: "If this film is a hoax, it's an incredibly clever one." And "incredibly" is not used loosely. Shortly after the showing in Vancouver, Patterson and Gimlin took the film to those who should know if anyone should whether a movie has been faked–the technicians in the special effects department at Universal Studios in Hollywood. These are the people who manufacture the King Kongs and Mighty Joe Youngs and other esoteric monsters of the screen. Patterson asked them to examine the film and tell him if they could reproduce it. Their conclusion was: "We could try. But we would have to create a completely new system of artificial muscles and find an actor who could be trained to walk like that. It might be done, but we would have to say that it would be almost impossible."

René has pursued the question of the film's authenticity relentlessly. Some of the experts he has shown it to, giving convincingly detailed reasoning (Chapter 9 and appendix), conclude it is real. Others, more cautious, say in effect: "It would be very difficult to say it is faked." And a few say it isn't real because it can't be. They offer no analysis of the film to support their rejection of it.

One of the observers was Don Grieve, Reader in biomechanics at London's Royal Free Hospital of Medicine, whom René sought out during his trip to Europe in 1971-72. The essence of Grieve's conclusions concerns the speed at which the film was shot. If it was taken at sixteen or eighteen frames per second (the speed usually used by amateur photographers) then Grieve says the combination of the creature's body movements are not compatible with those of any normal human gait. But if the camera was used at twenty-four frames per second (a setting used for special effects and for shooting TV documentaries), then he says "all the movements do fit together into a human-like combination.

"You could say the pattern is compatible with the movements of a man dressed in a skin (if it was at the faster speed). On the other hand I can't see any zipper. It looks realistic. I can see the muscle masses in the appropriate places and so on. If it is a fake, it is an extremely clever fake."

Grieve summed up his feelings about the film:

"My subjective impressions have oscillated between total acceptance of the Sasquatch on the grounds that the film would be difficult to fake, to ... irrational rejection based on an emotional response to the possibility that the Sasquatch actually exists. This seems worth stating because others have reacted similarly to the film. The possibility of a very clever fake cannot be ruled out on the evidence of the film. A man could have sufficient height and suitable proportions to mimic the longitudinal dimensions of the Sasquatch. The shoulder breadth however would be difficult to achieve without getting an unnatural appearance to the arms' swing and shoulder contours. The possibility of fakery is ruled out if the speed of the film was sixteen to eighteen fps. In these conditions a normal human being could not duplicate the observed pattern, which would suggest that the Sasquatch must possess a very different locomotor system to that of man." In the context of opinions to be presented in Chapter 9, Grieve's analysis becomes especially interesting.

It would be ideal from the point of view of the Sasquatch hunters to be able to say the Patterson film was shot at sixteen or eighteen fps. Unfortunately no one knows what the speed was. Patterson, right up to his death early in

1972, when he was little more than forty, said he just didn't know for sure what speed his camera was set for.

He was not by any means a professional photographer. On the other hand, he had from time to time talked of making a TV documentary about the search for the Sasquatch. So there must remain some doubt about the film. But if we cannot accept that the camera was set for the slower speed, then we have to consider the alternative conclusion–that Roger Patterson, ex-rodeo cowboy, small-time promoter and self-proclaimed seeker of the truth, somehow generated the funds and technical skill to create what the supreme experts virtually state would be impossible to create. It seems an unlikely alternative.

And what about Bob Gimlin? He has nothing to gain today by perpetuating a lie, and nothing to lose by exposing one. In fact there are undoubtedly those who would pay for conclusive evidence of a fake. Gimlin tells the story today just as it happened in October of 1967. Either he is a liar, or he too was gulled by Patterson while Patterson was achieving the technically impossible–or the film is authentic.

But we've moved ahead of what was happening to the film–and to those associated with it–after the Vancouver *première.*

In more than one way for René, the film had come as a shock. First, he had seen the object of his years of searching. That had rocked him. But what was hitting much harder was the thought that after fourteen years someone else–a virtual novice at that–would collect the glory and the hard cash prizes that he had always assumed would accrue to the first finder of the Sasquatch, and whom he had always determined would be himself. He was, as he puts it, "shattered." He needn't have been. The cynicism that had always followed the Sasquatch, though showing some signs of weakening in the wake of the film, was still sufficient to keep the issue at low priority in the realm of scientific studies. They still wanted bones. And without the boffins' endorsement no one was prepared to finance any further investigations, or even to offer more than a nominal sum for use of the film.

Life magazine was watching the proceedings and had a woman reporter in Vancouver. She was authorized to give Patterson five hundred dollars as a retainer against possible use by *Life* of the film. Following this up, Patterson and Gimlin went to New York for discussions and viewing of the film, with the idea that if *Life*'s experts were satisfied, a contract would be offered. The experts were scientists from the New York Museum of Natural History, but Patterson was not impressed with either their expertise or their attitude. He told René on his return:

"They viewed the film once only. I had the feeling that when they came into that room they were doing it only as a favour to *Life* magazine and that they already had their minds made up. There was everybody but the janitor there, looking and giggling. Then the scientists went into another room with the *Life* people where apparently they told the magazine staff that the film wasn't kosher. That was all–they left. Then it was shown to people at the Bronx Zoo. They said they thought there was something wrong with the film, but they never did say what it was. And of course they said: 'Mind you, if you ever do get one of these things, we'd sure like to take a look at it....' "

(*Life* magazine had a change of mind in December 1972, when one of its reporters spent several days with René in preparing the story for what was to have been a six-page colour spread on the Sasquatch, including the *Life* cover, early in 1973. The following week, *Life* was pronounced dead. Maybe the staff of *Life* had been impressed by the fact that on August 10th of 1972 the very formal *Wall Street Journal* had given the centre of its front page and a good part of two inside pages to a serious, balanced examination of the Sasquatch phenomenon, and that the *Sunday Times* in London on August 20th made it the top subject of its feature pages.)

Finally *Argosy* magazine ran the first published stills from the Patterson movie in February 1968, with a story by Ivan Sanderson.

"Maybe it was because it was *Argosy* and not *Life*," René speculates, "but there was still no scientist or institution that would take it on themselves to make a proper analysis of the thing–even to go and see the footprints it had left. It was unbelievable. We figured that after the story appeared there would be reserve-parking only along the road into Bluff Creek. Nothing happened. It had no impact whatsoever."

Finally Green paid $1,500 for the Canadian rights to the film and René agreed to share the costs. Out of the original twenty-four feet of film they produced 320 feet, running parts of it in repeat sequence and stop-frame to give extended exposure to certain areas. René made several swings through the northwest showing the documentary and lecturing on the subject, while Green stayed home and wrote his first booklet, *On The Track of The Sasquatch.* The tours never did more than a break-even business and finally were discontinued. Other rights to the film had been sold and it has since been shown on television networks in several countries, including Britain and Australia. An organization called American National Enterprizes still shows it regularly in the U.S.

Occasional opinions on the Patterson film have since floated forth from behind the walls of North American science. Usually they are brief, negative, and offered with little or no supporting argument.

In a letter dated November 26th, 1971, Richard W. Thorington Jr., who was at that time director of the Primate Biology Program at the Smithsonian Institute, said in reply to a query on why the Smithsonian scientists considered the film a joke: "...To them it appeared all too obvious that the pictures were made of a person dressed up in an ape costume, trying to run in an unnatural way. The one person who did not at the time consider this to be the case was Dr.

John Napier ... let me point out that there are two ways to look at the 'Bigfoot phenomenon.' One is the approach that Dr. Napier espoused that we should keep an open mind and review all evidence to decide whether this is a hoax or a legitimate area of study. The other approach, which I am forced to espouse is that one should demand a clear demonstration that there is such a thing as a Bigfoot before spending any time on the subject. There are many, many valid areas of research for which the subject matter is known to exist, so one should busy oneself with these rather than with will-of-the wisps."

The implication that Mr. Thorington Jr. was not prepared even to keep an open mind is extraordinary considering his presumed status as a probing researcher and considering the diametrically opposed posture of a colleague of at least equal stature, John Napier. What he meant by a "clear demonstration" can only be guessed at–a body, presumably. In other words, if one is laid at his feet he'll accept their existence–or at least *its* existence!

It's the kind of attitude that rattled Columbus when he was pushing the notion about the earth being round: it couldn't be, therefore it wasn't. René takes some satisfaction from remarking on the distinct lack of interest history has shown in preserving the names of those who jeered at that particular sailor.

Another authoritative opinion was heard in December of 1969 when the Canadian Press ran a story out of Ottawa quoting Philip Youngman, the curator of mammals at the Canadian National Museum of Natural Sciences. Youngman and others at the museum had seen the film and casts of footprints. Youngman said: "It's a hoax, no question ... I don't know how they can fake it ... but I'm convinced this movie and these footprints are fake.

"One of our scientists claims you could see a human heel under the skin of the creature as it walked...."

That last observation, in light of the combined theories of the American Grover Krantz and two Moscow scientists, could prove to be one of the most unsophisticated ever made on the subject by a supposed expert (the unnamed scientist).

Youngman's very firm opinion interested me. If he would expand on his reasoning it would provide my book with something of a balance for the predominantly "favouring" arguments, against which I had so far been able to collect only the "it's bosh" kind of undeveloped reaction. I wrote to him, explaining the project and asking him would he be prepared to write something for inclusion in the book. Youngman replied: "...I will gladly comment on the possibility of there being a Sasquatch, and especially on the footprints from California. I would like to know how my views might be used in your book. Would you quote me or would you use my writing under my name?"

My reply was that whatever Youngman had to say would be presented in full and fully attributed to him.

I didn't hear any more from Youngman, and two months later I again wrote to him, stressing that the book was well in progress and I was in need of his promised material. There was no reply. Finally I reached him by telephone. He said he had been overwhelmed by routine work but apologised for his tardiness and promised to write something for me "very soon." And then he added, *As a matter of fact I've been changing my mind about the Sasquatch question.*" He didn't elaborate, suggesting that the phone call had cost me enough already, and we parted on the understanding that within a few days Youngman's new views would be in my hands.

I haven't heard a word since then. I wrote two more letters, both of which were ignored. Whether Youngman jumped back over to the safe side of the fence, or is still dithering on the rails, I don't know. Whatever the case, I regret that he didn't pursue his commitment.

We started this chapter with the observation that 1967 is called "the big year." It was the Patterson film largely that qualified it for the title, but there were two other incidents that year which stimulated the search and which René considers outstanding in his records.

The first took place near the small Oregon town of The Dalles, a community that has since become the base for one full-time Sasquatch hunter, Peter Byrne.

One night in May of 1967 a group of youths were walking home when they became aware that something, or someone, was following a parallel path to theirs on a bluff that ran alongside the road. Every few yards, rocks rattled down the hillside towards them. Their first thought was that other boys were the culprits and they started off up the bank to check. As they did so, something started down the bank at them. They couldn't make out in the dark exactly what it was, but they could see enough to prompt them to make a sharp reverse and take off back down the slope. The ensuing events were described eventually for René by one of the youths, Dennis Taylor, who was nineteen at the time of the incident.

"We took off and ran into a field near the freeway. It came right on after us, busting right through the fence, and then it stopped. It was big–about eight or nine feet–and heavy. We watched it for about thirty seconds and then figured we'd better get to the freeway and get a car going into town. As we started moving, so did it; if we walked, it walked; if we ran, it ran, and if we stopped, it stopped. When we got onto the freeway it wouldn't follow us. We watched it from there for about two minutes.

"There was a bend in the freeway about half a mile away. A car came round that and in its headlights we saw another of these things crossing the freeway. We didn't know whether they were trying to sneak up on us or what, so we ran along to a motel, got a pickup truck there and went off to get some more kids at a café."

When they returned with reinforcements one of the creatures was halfway up the hillside. The youngsters, putting their confidence in numbers, took off after it armed with rocks and knives and sticks. The creature outdistanced them easily and disappeared. The gang went home, planning to return the next night, this time with guns. They did, and they saw one of the creatures, but only at a distance. On the third night they got much closer.

"We saw two of them," Dennis Taylor continued, "up on the bluff and we followed them with guns. When we got up there, one of them was less than ten feet away.

"Dave Churchill let it have it twice in the chest with double-ought shot from a 12-gauge shot gun. It fell down and rolled over and we thought for sure he had killed it. Then it got up and ran off, going right through a four-strand wire fence. It snapped three posts off flush with the ground. We decided we'd better not follow it. We came back the next day and photographed the fence and the tracks it left–they were nineteen inches long and eight-to-ten inches wide–and we tried to track it from the blood, but we lost the trail."

The youths returned on several occasions and once, they said, saw five of the creatures together at a distance.

Taylor's description of the thing fits the usual pattern, but this was one of the occasions when an offensive smell was associated with it. Taylor couldn't compare the smell with anything he had ever experienced. "It was sort of rancid. I guess the closest I could come to in comparing it would be to say maybe like a cow that had been dead for a couple of months." He also remembered that the eyes of the creatures glowed red when any light was aimed at them.

The area outside The Dalles where this happened is studded with old mines and natural caves and the youths believed this was where the creatures concealed themselves in daylight.

It's a startling story and again one in which the sincerity of the narrator(s) must to a large extent be the measure of its validity. They're young people, so the story becomes unfair game for the sort of snorting cynicism that, almost reflexively, associates youth with delinquency of one form or another. But listening to Dennis Taylor recount the events, strongly persuades one that the young man is describing what he clearly saw and heard and smelled. He makes no effort to dramatize the story, nor does he seem unduly concerned with the need to convince anyone of its truth. He tells it articulately, unhesitantly, and it is repeated here with the belief that he was not mistaken, nor indulging in fancy. And events that occurred near The Dalles four years later and involving a quite different group of persons, while not necessarily providing a "I-told-you-so" conclusion for Dennis Taylor's story, do tend to lend it credibility.

The other major event in 1967 took place in the hills behind Estacada, a tiny community about fifty miles southwest of The Dalles. It was at the end of October, just after the close of deer season. Glenn Thomas, a power-saw operator, had taken a break from the noise and fumes of his machine and walked off along a network of trails among the trees. He was at about the five-thousand-foot level and it was chilly, with the fog freezing on the trees. He had walked a mile or so, enjoying the quiet of the woods, when he came into a clearing, on the far side of which was a huge rock slide that had come down some years before.

The edge of the clearing was as far as he got.

He was halted by the sight of three hair-covered, humanlike creatures, two adults and a young one, digging among the rocks. They were less than a hundred feet away and in their endeavours had not heard his approach.

They were moving the rocks, quickly and quietly, and stacking them in neat piles. As they turned the rocks over, before stacking them, they sniffed each one carefully before laying it down and moving on to the next one. Their purpose soon became clear. They were hunting marmots, or rock rabbits, and eating each rodent as it was unearthed.

"They didn't skin them or anything," Thomas recalls, "just started cramming the head in their mouths. Maybe they bit them in two. The little one didn't get any help from the adults; it had to get its own."

At one stage, the male adult (Thomas was sure the mature ones were a male and a female) began to throw out rocks at a great speed, the only occasion on which it abandoned the concern for quiet. It came up with a handful of grass–what Thomas later took to be a nest–with several small rodents in it. These the creatures ate quickly. It was about then that they became aware of their observer. They looked round at him briefly then quickly moved off over the rock pile and disappeared.

"They were fast and they were strong," Thomas says. "The adults were slinging out boulders that no ordinary man could lift. And they seemed to pick up the rocks without using their thumbs; just wrapped the whole hand around them."

Thomas estimated he watched them at work for about fifteen minutes: "Although I wasn't really giving much thought to the time–I was mainly thinking that I'd gone crazy...lost my marbles."

He described them as looking "like humans with hair all over. They had no clothes. The male was a lot heavier than what I took to be the female. They were both heavy in the legs and the small of the backs was particularly stout. The male had longer hair, more ragged, down on its shoulders.

"The small one didn't come up to the mother's waist, just about up to her hips, and the mother didn't seem to be more than six feet tall. The male could have been quite a bit bigger than that, but I don't think he would go much over four hundred pounds. All of them had patches on their face which seemed to have no hair."

Apart from the "family" situation, Thomas's description is especially interesting because of two elements.

He remarks that the creatures did not use their thumbs in grasping the rocks. In Prof. Boris Porshnev's list of characteristics of the Russian Almas there is the note that the creature's thumb has "less opposition" than that found in man, meaning that grasping would likely be done with a wrap-around position of the whole hand.

And the exercise of hunting for rock rabbits is almost identical to a description of the activities of a Yeti in Ralph Izzard's book *The Abominable Snowman Adventure,* the account of the 1953 *Daily Mail* expedition which started the fire in René Dahinden. There the small rodent is called a pica (translated in the book as "rock rabbit"), and the method of unearthing it and its quick disposal are the same as what Glenn Thomas saw.

The Patterson film and the events at The Dalles and Estacada were the essence of the big year.

The biggest year had yet to come.

CHAPTER 7

René had expected the Patterson film to change the whole tone of the Sasquatch issue. When it didn't the effect on him was two-edged. First there was the depressingly enveloping anti-climax, the thought that, "My God, what *do* you have to show them before they'll take it seriously?"– "they" being the science authorities who were, in most cases, content to let the film slip into the Sasquatch files with the rest of the rejected data. On the other hand if the film, as it seemed to René, was not faked, then the game was still very much on, and wide open. In effect the reluctance of science to become directly involved with Patterson was something of a reprieve for René.

He did not rush back to Bluff Creek. While the incident had not drawn to the area quite the crowds he had predicted it would, there were a few of the curious stumbling about in the bush, and René concluded that his added presence would hardly encourage the creature to make another appearance.

Through the spring of 1968 he worked on his freelance shot-retrieving, building up a stake for the next move that summer–a prolonged expedition into the raw country of British Columbia's Garibaldi Provincial Park, a 750 square mile mountain wilderness which runs north from the Fraser Valley behind the small towns of Haney and Mission.

With two companions he spent sixty-eight days exploring the park from August through October. From a base camp in a cave they hiked countless miles along the mountain ridges, the snowfields and glaciers. They saw no trace of their quarry.

René came out of the bush, disappointed perhaps but far from discouraged. The fact that they had found nothing was no proof that what they sought was not there. By now he had experienced the extremes of optimism and crashed hopes and was of the simple determination that he had a path to follow and that he was going on to its end, whatever that might be. He would continue checking reports, old and new, and put his faith in persistence. He worked that winter at odd jobs and was back on the Vancouver Gun Club site in the early spring when news broke of an incident nearby in Washington State.

Just before 4 a.m. on March 5 (1969), Don Cox left his home in Washougal, Skamania County, heading for some salmon fishing. He was alone in his car. As he rounded a bend on Highway 14, about one mile east of Beacon Rock State Park, he saw in the morning fog what he described as "an ape-faced dark-coloured creature" crossing the road in front of him. Cox told police later: "I was heading toward Hamilton Island (on the Columbia River) to fish for salmon, and I had just come out of a fog bank that had caused me to slow my car down when I saw what first appeared to be a tree leaning towards the middle of the road. I slowed my car further and turned my headlights to high beam, and it was then I saw this fur-covered human form with a face like an ape. He ran across the road in front of the car, leaped up a forty-degree bank and disappeared in the woods.

"I was really shook up when I reached North Bonneville where I stopped at a café and ordered coffee. A waitress called the county sheriff's office when I told her my story."

Deputy sheriff John Mason was sent to investigate and he and Cox returned to the site. Cox told Mason the creature had been more than eight feet tall. Mason later reported that Cox was "stone sober but obviously shaken by his experience." The pair could find no definable footprints but could see that some large creature had gone up the bank. At one spot in a smeared print there were visible toe marks–not claw marks. The print was eight feet up the bank from the road.

Cox's sighting took place about forty miles south of Mt. St. Helens, the home of Ape Canyon, which also lies in Skamania County, and about thirty-five miles west of The Dalles, Oregon. There are only two incorporated towns in Skamania County, Stevenson, the county seat, and North Bonneville, and the county's total population is between five thousand and six thousand, most of whom live close to the Columbia River. Skamania County is exceptionally rugged country and much of its mountainous terrain is pocked with caves bequeathed by some long-dead volcanic upheavals. New caves are constantly being discovered. They have been known since before early settler days as the Ape Caves.

The Cox story was eventually a main feature in a special issue that summer of the weekly Skamania County *Pioneer*. The front page featured an artist's concept of the creature Cox saw, drawn with the aid of police identi-kits. The sketches show a fuzzy, humanoid form in various action positions. Cox evidently made no attempt to elaborate beyond what he was able to see within the limits imposed by the pre-dawn fog.

The editor of the *Pioneer* and officers of the sheriff's department, all of whom knew Cox well, emphasized that they accepted and believed his story.

Subsequent sightings of footprints in the mountains nearby were checked by the sheriff's office along with experienced outdoorsmen of the area. The *Pioneer* says of the investigation:

> Seven miles from any habitation they found "Bigfoot" prints, emerging (from) a canyon, crossing a snow-covered forest trail, proceeding through a logged-over area or clear-cut, and headed towards the lava beds.
>
> There were no snowmobile tracks, no ski tracks, no snowshoe tracks–no people tracks of any kind. They returned convinced that something out of the ordinary had been there.

It was speculated that the particularly hard winter of 1968-69, the worst on record in the area, had driven the creatures down the mountains, well below their usual zone of habitation, in search of food and possibly shelter.

One family stated quite determinedly that one of the "things" lived close to their home all winter. They said it had been heard making its high-pitched calls in the nearby hills and that when this happened their big watch dog, normally the most aggressive of animals, was reduced to a trembling coward. Though its hackles rose, it refused to budge from the back yard. The same family found huge logs tossed aside, as if by something of giant strength searching for insects or nocturnal small mammals. Other reports told of rabbits quietly killed and removed from hutches in remote areas.

In a March edition of the *Pioneer* there was a picture of Skamania County sheriff Bill Closner and deputy Jack Wright examining a footprint which they later cast. It was twenty-two inches long, seven and a half inches across the ball of the foot, and four and a half inches at the heel. After casting the print, sheriff Closner said, "I guess I'm going to have to stop laughing."

The incidents of the early months of 1969, considered along with the history of the creature in the area, were enough to provoke official action. The following ordinance was compiled and was published on April 4th:

ORDINANCE NO. 69-01

Be it hereby ordained by the Board of County Commissioners of Skamania County:

WHEREAS, there is evidence to indicate the possible existence in Skamania County of a nocturnal primate mammal variously described as an ape-like creature or a sub-species of Homo Sapiens, and

WHEREAS, both legend and purported recent sightings and spoor support this possibility, and

WHEREAS, this creature is generally and commonly known as a "Sasquatch", "Yeti", "Bigfoot", or "Giant Hairy Ape", and

WHEREAS publicity attendant upon such real or imagined sightings has resulted in an influx of scientific investigators as well as casual hunters, many armed with lethal weapons, and

WHEREAS, the absence of specific laws covering the taking of specimens encourages laxity in the use of fire-arms and other deadly devices and poses a clear and present threat to the safety and well-being of persons living or travelling within the boundaries of Skamania County as well as to the creatures themselves,

THEREFORE BE IT RESOLVED that any premeditated, wilful and wanton slaying of any such creature shall be deemed a felony punishable by a fine not to exceed Ten Thousand Dollars ($10,000.00) and/or imprisonment in the county jail for a period not to exceed Five (5) years.

BE IT FURTHER RESOLVED that the situation existing constitutes an emergency and as such this ordinance is effective immediately.

ADOPTED this 1st day of April 1969.

Board of Commissioners of Skamania County. By: Conrad Lundy Jr., Chairman.

Approved: Robert K. Leick, Skamania County Prosecuting Attorney.

The ordinance impressed some of the Sasquatch hunters. It didn't impress René–not favourably, anyway.

"It's amazing," he says. "Here they are laying down ten thousand dollar fines and five-year jail sentences for the shooting of something that most authorities say can't possibly exist. What the hell is the point in protecting something that we haven't found yet?"

His tart response may be linked to speculation that the Skamania County authorities had their ears tuned much more to the music of a publicity bandwagon than to any song of distress from the mountains when they signed the ordinance.

The Skamania County business settled down and René, having collected all he could in the way of evidence, returned to Vancouver. He would next be back in Washington State that summer on the heels of the incident involving deputy sheriff Verlin Herrington, discussed in Chapter 2.

Before René went to Herrington, he spent several days talking to the people in the Copalis Beach area, eliciting their opinions about the policeman. While doing this he heard rumours of unusual happenings on the Tahola Indian reserve about twenty miles to the north, which prompted him to pay a visit. Arriving at the reserve and explaining his purpose, he was directed from the village office to the foreman of a Seattle construction outfit, Western Sewer Construction, that was installing a water system for the village.

The foreman, Frank Pfau, confirmed that there had indeed been some odd goings on, and agreed to take René to the site. Before he started the truck he took a large calibre rifle from a rack in the cab and set it on the seat between them, looking somewhat embarrassed as he did so. They drove back a little way to a hillside where the crew had been capping wells and constructing catch basins. They had set to clearing an area in the very dense bush and the work had gone well for a couple of days. Then the attacks had started–rocks flying from deep in the bush and rattling past the labourers. The first thought was that kids from the village were horsing about–until someone pointed out that the rocks weighed between four and five pounds and were coming in with healthy velocity and *uphill*, from quite a way in the bush. Several of the crew had refused to continue the work.

René returned to the village and asked the Indians about it. They shrugged, said there was nothing terribly unusual

136

about it, that the same thing happened frequently to them while fishing the Quinalt River, and that the rocks were flung by the Stick Indians, or Sasquatches, who were indicating anger against intruders into their territory. One of the villagers with the colourful name of Inky Charlie, a well-known hunting and fishing guide in northwest Washington State, said the place abounded with strange cries from the bush, cries that belonged to no wildlife that he had ever seen or known of–apart from the Sasquatch, whose existence he didn't question.

A search in the area of the rock-throwing, conducted by armed police accompanied by René and several of the construction crew, failed to turn anything up. Before René left the village however, he was taken aside by the young resident preacher, also an Indian, and advised in very firm tones that he was involving himself with something that would be much better left alone, that only a great–though unspecified–evil could come of further pursuit of the matter, and that he should drop it then and there.

Whatever the preacher meant by his rather sketchy warning was filed by René as interesting incidental material for the Sasquatch file. He didn't permit it to slow him down. The year, 1969, was beginning to show a lot of promise. In fact it became what is now referred to as "the biggest year."

On August 12th, near the small California town of Oroville, where some sixty years before the last of the Yahi tribe, Ishi, had been found huddled by a slaughter-house fence, Charles Jackson was out in the untidy yard of his small farm, along with his six-year-old son. It was about 9.30 p.m. and the pair were burning a drum of trash, including a mess of rabbit entrails from animals they had killed earlier that day.

Standing watching the flames, they suddenly heard a rumbling noise behind them, "as if," Jackson said, "something was trying to knock (an old outbuilding) down." Turning quickly, they saw by the old building, no more than fifteen feet from them, what Jackson a few days later described to René as "an ape; but like a human. It had grey hair, glossy, with light tips, almost silver, and huge pendulous breasts. It stood a good eight feet tall."

Briefly, the man and the boy and the creature faced each other: "It had a quizzical look, sort of puzzled, at first, as if it was wondering what we were doing. Later, I thought it must have been near man before. It wasn't alarmed by us."

But that was later. Jackson's response, as soon as he recovered from the immediate shock, was to push the boy ahead of him and rush for the house. "We were both frightened," he said.

They weren't the only ones frightened. Jackson had three dogs–outdoor dogs who wouldn't retreat from any bear as they had frequently proven. One whined briefly, then raced into the house and went to ground in the bedroom. The other two didn't even whine. They took off at a dead run and also found cover somewhere in the house. Jackson said they had never in their lives acted in such a fashion.

He gathered up his family, piled them into the car, and headed for Oroville where he reported the happenings to the police. Whether the police thought Jackson had dumped his family in the car and raced into town with the story just as a joke, isn't recorded. But the police didn't go to the house until the following day (the Jacksons returned, reluctantly, in the early hours of the morning). They found no traces of the creature–the summer-dry ground was too hard for any prints–and Jackson got the impression that they had come out to laugh rather than to look.

René got there just less than a week after the incident (the Oroville *Mercury Register* had picked the story up, presumably from routine checks of police blotters, and it had appeared in papers further north), and Jackson recalled further details about the creature:

"It was like both an ape and a human. It had longer legs than a man. It was upright and when it walked away later it swung its arms like a human. The chest area and the face were almost bare and the face was like that of a negro, the skin almost black. Its palms were paler, almost yellowish. At the shoulder it was between three and four feet wide and there were huge bulging muscles, and no neck. Its arms were massive, very muscular, and it had long fingers.

"It had great flat breasts that hung down to the navel area. The hair on its head was like that of a woman who hadn't washed it for months. It was light grey with what seemed to be caked mud on it. Its feet were about fourteen to fifteen inches long and were very flat and very wide."

René spent three weeks in the Oroville area, much of the time with Jackson, going over the story repeatedly, watching for inconsistencies, finding none. Jackson said he had never before heard of such a creature, had never heard of the Sasquatch or Bigfoot phenomenon. Beyond reporting his story to the police, Jackson sought no publicity over the matter. After the lengthy discussions with the man, René could only conclude that, "His story impressed me all to hell."

In view of the Jackson incident it's worth recording here another story that René came across at the same time. It is repeated here as it appeared on the front page of the *Weekly Butte Record* of Oroville on the morning of Saturday, November 5th, 1870: "The Wild Man of Crow Canyon."

A correspondent of the Antioch *Ledger,* writing from Grayson under date of October 16th says:

I saw in your paper, a short time since, an item concerning the "gorilla," which was said to have been seen in Crow Canyon and shortly after in the mountains at Orestimba Creek. You sneered at the idea of there being any such a "crittur" in these hills, and, were I not better informed, I should sneer too, or else conclude that one of your recent prospecting party had got lost in the wilderness and did not have any sense enough to find his way back....

I positively assure you that this gorilla or wildman, or whatever you choose to call it, is no myth. I know that it exists, and that there are at least two of them, having seen them both at once not a year ago. Their existence has been reported at times for the past twenty years and I have heard it said that in early days an orang-outang escaped from a ship on the southern coast; but the creature I have seen is not that animal, and if it is, where did he get his mate?...

Last fall I was hunting in the mountains about twenty miles south of here, and camped five or six days in one place, as I have done every season for the past fifteen years. Several times I returned to camp, after a hunt, and saw that the ashes and charred sticks from the fireplace had been scattered about. An old hunter notices such things and very soon gets curious to know the cause.

Although my bedding and traps and little stores were not disturbed, as I could see, I was anxious to learn who or what it was that so regularly visited my camp, for clearly the half-burned sticks and cinders could not scatter themselves about. I saw no tracks near the camp as the hard ground covered with leaves would show none.

So I started in a circle round the place, and, three hundred yards off, in damp sand, I struck the tracks of a man's feet, as I supposed–bare and of immense size. Now I *was* curious, sure, and I resolved to lay for the bare-footed visitor. I accordingly took a position on a hillside about sixty or seventy feet from the fire, and securely hid in the bush, I waited and watched.

Two hours or more I sat there and wondered if the owner of the feet would come again, and whether he imagined what an interest he had created in my enquiring mind, and finally what possessed him to be prowling about there with no shoes on.

The fireplace was on my right, and the spot where I saw the track was on my left, hid by the bushes. It was in this direction my attention was mostly directed, thinking the visitor would appear there....

Suddenly I was startled by a shrill whistle, such as

boys produce with two fingers under their tongue, and turning quickly, I ejaculated, "Good God!" as I saw the object of my solicitude standing beside my fire, erect, and looking suspiciously around.

It was in the image of man, but it could not have been human. I was never so benumbed with astonishment before. The creature, whatever it was, stood fully five feet high, and disproportionately broad and square at the foreshoulders, with arms of great length. The legs were very short, and the body long. The head was small compared with the rest of the creature, and appeared to be set upon his shoulders without a neck. The whole was covered with dark brown and cinnamon coloured hair, quite long in some parts; that on the head standing in a shock and growing close down to the eyes, like a Digger Indian's.

As I looked he threw his head back and whistled again, and then stooped and grasped a stick from the fire. This he swung round, until the fire on the end had gone out, when he repeated the manoeuvre. I was dumb, almost, and could only look.

Fifteen minutes I sat and watched him as he whistled and scattered my fire about. I could easily have put a bullet through his head, but why should I kill him?

Having amused himself, apparently as he desired, with my fire, he started to go, and having gone a short distance he returned, and was joined by another–a female, unmistakeably–when they both turned and walked past me, within twenty yards of where I sat, and disappeared in the brush.

I could not have had a better opportunity for observing them, as they were unconscious of my presence. Their only object in visiting my camp seemed to be to amuse themselves with swinging lighted sticks around.

I have told this story many times since then and it has often raised an incredulous smile; but I have met one person who has seen the mysterious creatures, and a dozen who have come across their tracks....

There are considerable discrepancies between the physical proportions of this creature and the one described by Charles Jackson, but the basic characteristics are the same. And the differences, rather than providing extra fuel for the skeptics, could be argued to support the thesis that Jackson's story and others like it are certainly not simply repeats of tales they may have heard, as is frequently claimed.

The incredulous smiles that the author met with are still around today. So are the tracks and, evidently, the creatures that made them.

While René was investigating the Jackson story, action was starting much further north and east of him. The Big Horn dam was under construction on the North Saskatchewan River, just west of the Alberta community of Nordegg, and construction workers were reporting seeing hairy giants walking along a nearby ridge. Added strength was given to the stories by a band of Hobbema Indians who had left their reserve south of Edmonton to move into the wilds and live in "the old way." They spoke–reluctantly at first–of their familiarity with the creature and they told of seeing it on many occasions and of the many footprints they had encountered the previous year while in summer camp on the Kootenay Plains.

Leaving Oroville, René made his way to the dam site and eventually, at a foreman's suggestion, started work on the job alongside construction men who claimed to have seen the giant–and it *was* a giant if their estimates are correct.

René's special interest became known and those with something to tell began coming to him, especially the Indians who were intrigued by the thought of a white man dedicated to finding the creature that played such a big part in their folklore. They were much more willing to talk with René than with John Green, who also had appeared at the dam. Green had had the poor judgment to let it be known that any Sasquatch stepping into the range of his rifle, would be a dead one. This did not sit well with the Indians whose thoughts, guided partly perhaps by ancient tales of the creature's supernatural powers, were that it should be protected, for both its benefit and theirs.

René showed the Patterson film to the Indians, who responded with the opinion that "their" creature was less bulky than the one on the film, less hairy, and much taller. According to the testimony of the construction men who watched the creature, first as it sat against a ridge and then as it walked three-quarters of a mile or so along the ridge, the Indians' "much taller" description becomes a remarkable understatement.

The witnesses estimated its height at between twelve and fifteen feet.

The creature was first seen by nineteen-year-old Guy L'Heureux and seventeen-year-old Harley Peterson, who were working on a pumphouse below the dam. Eventually they were joined by three others, Harley's father, Stan Peterson, Floyd Engen, and an education student, Dale Boddy.

Harley described the scene later for a reporter from the Edmonton *Journal*:

"The figure sat for about fifteen minutes, then it stood up, looked around and walked away.

"It looked enormous. Its head was bent slightly forward and it looked very hefty. We watched it for about three-quarters of a mile as it made its way round a ridge."

Dale Boddy insisted it could not have been a bear:

"It was too tall and its legs too thin ... and a bear couldn't have walked that far on its hind legs, and not at that speed. It seemed to be taking six-foot strides and it covered the distance in less than two minutes."

Floyd Engen said:

"I just didn't believe it ... I took off my glasses and looked again. But there it was. I knew I was wide awake. I jumped up on a tractor and waved my hat at it and yelled. It didn't seem to notice."

The creature was about half a mile away from the men and they had nothing such as binoculars with which to pick out detail. Nor at first did they realize just how big the thing was; when they did, they were stunned.

Two of the group went up to the ridge and retraced the creature's various movements, while the others watched from the pump house and made notes. They said they had noted the creature's height against some trees as it walked away; the men now following the same route were evidently less than half its height. The same conclusion was reached by checking against a number of other landmarks. They had been watching–if we are to accept all their reasoning–a creature that stood between twelve and fifteen feet in height.

It's a tall story indeed. Too tall for René Dahinden to accept without reservation. While he doesn't question the fact that the men saw something unusual, which might have been a Sasquatch, he does not accept the estimate of its height. His conclusion is that there is something about the topography, something he can't pin down, which encourages exaggerated estimates of object-heights. He noted that trees which looked quite tall from a distance were actuall; not so tall when one approached them. And he believes the particular line of sight from the men to what they saw also lent itself to misleading estimates of size. Oddly enough John Green took the opposite view. It was his opinion that all the estimates did indeed make sense and the creature was as tall as the men claimed.

The country around the dam site does not offer the best concealment, being lightly treed and comparatively open. But nothing further was seen either by searchers in small planes or by people on foot who investigated. However, one must consider that the area they were able to cover was only a tiny fraction of that extending in all directions from the Big Horn dam.

The only ones who expressed no doubt about the incident were the five workmen involved, and the Indians, who take the Sasquatch for granted.

For René it soon would be supplanted by something of much more substance as the biggest year took its course.

CHAPTER 8

In the recent past, Sasquatch research has been conducted by poorly financed, untrained, dedicated men.
A Sasquatch hunt with these people reminds one of a
Humphrey Bogart movie... in which a number of individuals having idiosyncratic and conflicting goals
cooperate sporadically to bring a mutual goal closer to
attainment. The goal however is mutual only in the
sense that each man wants to find a Sasquatch, and not
in the sense that each man wants somebody to find a
Sasquatch.*

Though Mr. Ondrack didn't know it, when he made that
observation he was reciting the perfect prologue to a series
of events that were even then started on their course, more
than two hundred miles southwest of Banff in the small
Washington community of Bossburg. Before these events
were concluded, the nature of the Sasquatch hunter would
have been placed on full and fascinating display and a sce-
nario would have evolved which, while falling well short of
Bogart quality, certainly would display much of the style
and dimension of a Hollywood special. By the time they
were over, René would have learned a great deal about his
colleagues in the hunt–and they about him; one of the
dedicated would have produced a film of the Sasquatch, the
authenticity of which, to say the least, would remain firmly
unconfirmed. And an officer of the United States border

---

* (From "The Sasquatch Phenomenon in Alberta," a paper presented to the
Western Association of Sociology and Anthropology, in Banff, Alberta, in
December 1969, by Jack W. Ondrack of the University of Alberta.)

145

patrol would predict a climax of the kind generally associated with the two-reel western movie. Ironically, the melodrama–for such it was, within a framework of farce–would be acted out virtually on top of that particular piece of evidence which, more so than any other, Napier uses to establish his contention that the Sasquatch lives.

René continued working at the Big Horn dam site, talking especially with the Indians, recording all he could of what they felt and thought and knew about the Sasquatch. In late November a phone call came from John Green, telling him that down in Bossburg, Ivan Marx, late of the Slick expedition, was hot on the trail of what appeared to be a crippled Sasquatch. By now not one to be exploded into the hunt at every mention of a track, René called Marx and discussed what had been found. He took three days to consider the details, then took off for Bossburg.

The tracks had first been found on November 24 by Joe Rhodes, a butcher from nearby Colville. They were in the soft soil near the Bossburg community garbage dump, and one foot appeared to be badly crippled. It was being speculated that the creature was handicapped badly enough to force it to scrounge off man's kitchen scraps for a living–a theory which René rejects.

When René arrived, it was to find the ground, and most of the prints, badly trampled by the dozens of locals who had been drawn to the scene when the news leaked out. The site was in the area of several Sasquatch sightings reported earlier that year, during one of which a woman had rushed into the sheriff's office, alarmed and frightened by two of the creatures she had seen on the highway, the main road from southeastern B.C. down to Spokane. Two deputies had made a casual check of the area but had spent most of the time ridiculing the woman's story before an officer of the border patrol. That is, they had scoffed, as the border patrol told it, until they noticed it was growing dark, at which stage, showing definite signs of nervousness, they had left.

René found one good print which someone had protected by covering it with a cardboard box. It was a right foot and clearly showed signs of malformation. He photographed it and cast a plaster mould. The next few days he spent surveying the area and the people who lived there, talking with all he met, making trips into the bush, and generally getting the feel of the whole situation. Within a few days he was joined by Bob Titmus, the taxidermist, and late leader of the abortive Tom Slick expedition, who had been living in Kitimat, B.C., some seven hundred miles north and west. The actors were gathering, and the performance that would ensue was perhaps foreshadowed by Titmus's behaviour immediately following his arrival and which René describes:

"He went out and bought an eight-pound slab of beef and hung it in a tree. I believe he was sitting out there at night in his panel truck, watching the meat, and thinking that if this thing *was* a cripple and *was* living off the garbage dump, when it came along he would just grab it by the arse and throw it in the truck and run off home with it."

Titmus had provided the Sasquatch's main course. Trotting along with the dessert came one Norm Davis (known to the company as "Dickie"), a radio station owner turned Sasquatch hunter for the time being. He hung a basket of fruit in a neighbouring tree, carefully suspending it a measured six feet from the ground, the height which, presumably, would afford the Sasquatch maximum viewing of the selection of goodies. René watched the antics, interested to the extent that they demonstrated once more the kind of frivolous approach he had become used to dealing with.

After three days, when the meat was about ready to make its own tracks and the bloom was off the fruit, Titmus gave up in disgust and went home to Kitimat. René, intrigued by the one crippled print and anxious to stay, made a deal with Davis: he would live in a trailer owned by the radio man and in lieu of rent would show the Patterson film and talk about the Sasquatch to local service clubs and other interested groups. The crippled print bothered him; he had never seen anything like it, and the more he considered it, the more unlikely it seemed that it could be anything but genuine. Davis's trailer was moved onto Ivan Marx's property and the hunters took up the pursuit. On the morning of December 13, a Saturday, they found what they were looking for.

Several inches of snow had covered the ground that morning when René and Ivan Marx and a young local man named Jim Hopkins set out in Marx's car to check an area along the banks of Roosevelt Lake, the reservoir for the Grand Coolie dam. They checked the bank for about four miles, examining spots where meat scraps had been dropped by René earlier in off-the-beat locations, but found nothing. Near a railway crossing, where the railroad and the highway run close to the Columbia River, they stopped and Marx climbed out to check a small meat cache a little way along a side road. Just before stopping, they had passed a jeep parked by the roadside. Marx was away from the car only seconds before he came racing back:

"Bigfoot tracks!" he shouted.

René was filling his pipe. He kept on filling it, peering over the bowl at Marx, waiting for the kicker, the grin that would say, "Okay, joke over." It didn't come. Instead Marx jumped into the car, whipped it round, and headed back down the road, rapping out in his excitement that he needed photographic equipment.

Dahinden's first thought as they roared down the highway was of the people in the jeep they had passed. Hyper-alert to the possibility of hoaxers, he considered them immediate suspects. With this in mind he told Jim to check the jeep's licence plates and Ivan to look for anyone he might recognize in the vehicle. Between them they were able to identify the occupants and later asked them if they happened to have seen the tracks. "Yes," they said, they had. And what had been their response? "We got the hell out of there–fast."

The three were quickly down to Marx's place and back to the tracks, cameras and–in René's case–a gun cocked and loaded for Sasquatch. Now for the first time René saw a full spread of the cripple's tracks. They were, and are still, among the most convincing tangible evidence to be turned up in his years as a Sasquatch hunter. The left footprint measured 17½ inches long, 6½ inches across the ball of the foot, and 5½ inches across the heel; the right one was 16½ inches long, 7 inches across the ball, and also 5½ inches at the heel. The right foot was deformed; the third toe was either badly twisted over or was missing, there being only a slight impression in the snow at its base; the little toe stuck out at a sharp angle; and the whole foot curved outwards and showed two distinct lumps on the outer edge. A careful count eventually showed there were 1,089 clearly definable prints on the path that the three followed through the snow.

The tracks led them from the river, across the railroad and across the main highway. Whatever had made them had stepped over a forty-three-inch-high, five-strand wire fence, judging by the single prints of the left and the right feet on either side of the fence. On the far side of the fence, in a cluster of pine trees, there was a marked depression in the ground among the pine needles, apparently where some heavy animal had rested. No one denies the possibility that this was made by a cow or a deer, there being plenty of each in the area, but its presence in the line of the crippled tracks is worth noting, as is the fact that right in the centre of the depression was a clump of snow holding the imprint of the toes of the left foot, as though the snow had been shaken loose after building up on the foot. In the clearing beyond the pine trees were hundreds more tracks, leading across the flat land and up a small hillside. In the heat of what appeared might be the moment of truth, René, discarding his customary caution, cried, "Now we're going to get that hairy sonofabitch!"

He figured the prints were going to lead on up the hill

and the hunters would be able to run whatever had made them into the ground. But the prints stopped, halfway up the hill, turned, and retraced their path downward. At one spot, between two side-by-side prints, the hunters discovered a deep yellow patch in the snow, apparently urine. It was probably against their interests that they neglected to collect the yellow snow; analysis may have given some clue as to what made it. The prints continued down the hill, parallel with their first ascending path, returned to the fence and crossed it again about fifty feet from the first step-over. From there the tracks led the hunters across the road and back and over the fence several times, and eventually across the road and the railroad, through a patch of bush and to the edge of a steep part of the river bank, about one hundred and fifty feet above the water. There the bank was overhanging. The tracks turned and went upstream for approximately two hundred feet, to a point where the bank sloped gradually down to the river, and there they stopped. All the way down the bank was a deep groove, as one made by a heel and a foot acting as a brake for an upright body "skiing" down the bank. Below that there was just rocks; no further markings.

One thought hammered repeatedly in Dahinden's mind, the thought that had prompted his earlier optimistic exclamation: the tracks were fresh, not more than fifteen hours old. He had checked the area the previous evening and it had been bare. Nevertheless, his characteristic caution was at work again. He was stirred all right, but his mind persisted in herding suspicions and pushing them to the front. Why did the tracks happen to be just there, where he would be sure to go every day, where he checked all the time, within a few miles of the garbage dump where the thing had been reported seen all the time? It was the obvious place for a hoaxer to plant his work. On the other hand it seemed impossible that anyone could have faked such minute anatomical detail as was evident in the crippled print. He walked the route of the tracks seven times, examining every

150

print, puzzling over them. Assuming they were real, where had the thing come from, and where had it gone to? Had it crossed the river upstream or downstream, and if so, how far away in which of those directions? (There are numerous reports in the history of the Sasquatch of the creatures swimming rivers and lakes.) The questions were obvious, and easy to ask, but were impossible to answer, given the group's limited resources. Dahinden, applying lessons he had learned at places such as Bluff Creek (where people, seeing a print, had sprinted off in every conceivable direction looking for its owner, leaving the print to the ravages of the first rain shower or the first curious onlooker and his dog), concentrated on the footprints, trying to deduce as much as possible from them.

The right print showed more compression than the left, suggesting that the body weight was more to the right, further suggesting that the right leg was shorter than the left as a result of whatever mishap–congenital or otherwise–had caused the evident malformation. René speculated that the creature had at one time suffered an accident that had caused dislocation of the shin bone. Some of the prints were lifted from the snow and kept in Marx's freezer for a while. They were eventually discarded when the hunters developed one of their periodic collective depressions, generally attributed to science's marked apathy towards their endeavours. As it was, their interest would soon be riveted on another freezer and its alleged contents.

René's preoccupation with the prints disturbed Norm (Dickie) Davis. Rather than worry about establishing the legitimacy of old ones, Davis thought, they should be out chasing new ones. Accordingly, he phoned Titmus and others and suggested that René was neglecting the hunt, that their presence was needed to get things back into gear. While they went about setting their affairs straight in their various locations before moving on Bossburg, the prints continued to attract general interest. Tourists tramped about, their curiosity tweaked by news stories, as did most of the sheriff's office members and officers from the border patrol. A bus driver on the Trail, B.C.-to-Spokane run, something of a Sasquatch buff himself, caught sight of René one day just off the highway filming the cripple's prints. He slammed on his brakes, hauling the bus to a halt just before the railway crossing, then reversed a hundred yards or so and drew the bus into the side of the road. Then, briefly explaining to his passengers that there were some Sasquatch tracks he had to see, he left them gaping out of the windows while he trotted over with his box camera to record his own souvenir of the malformed foot.

Five days after the finding of the tracks, a U.S. border patrol man discovered sets of what appeared to be the same ones on the far side of the river, presumably where the thing had either entered or left the water. These tracks were in an area normally closed to all but a logging company's personnel and, unfortunately, they were to a great extent washed out by recent rains. There were the toe marks, seemingly matching the cripple's, but little else that could be defined.

By this time René had been joined by Roy Fardell from B.C. and Roger St. Hilaire, a young zoologist from San Francisco. Together they considered the question of faking: on this side of the river the prints were perfectly located for discovery; on the other side they were in a spot virtually never used, where all the access gates were kept locked by the logging company. If the prints on this side had been faked, surely whoever had made them would have planted the ones on the far bank in an equally accessible place, to complete the hoax. (This persistent reversion into pessimism over tracks and other evidence is as much a constant of the serious Sasquatch hunter's character as his determination to resolve the mystery.) The consensus–while it remained firm–was that the tracks were genuine.

At this point Roger Patterson, with his partner Dennis Jensen, came to Bossburg. He would be there intermittently during the saga that followed; Jensen would hang in the whole time, protecting their dual interests.

The search for the cripple went on through December and into January. Using four-wheel drive vehicles, light planes, and snowmobiles, the hunters covered hundreds of square miles of rugged country, ploughing over mountain ridges and through dense bush. And all the time René lived with the wriggling thought that maybe they were following a phoney. The longer they went without finding a trace of the cripple, the worse the suspicions grew, and the more the others began to share the doubts. Misgivings went around the group like the Hong Kong flu as each of the hunters nurtured doubts about the others. Infidelities were imagined, old and forgotten conflicts resurrected. As it happened, it wasn't each other they had to worry about–at that point anyway.

In January René took another shot at making the Patterson film pay, this time on a showing circuit of the Calgary area. He would be a distant but pivotal participant in the main feature.

One evening at the end of January, two men arrived at the Sasquatch hunters' camp on the Marx property, Joe Metlow, a prospector, and Bill Streeter, a state wildlife agent. Metlow's first question to the hunters was, what was their price on a Sasquatch? It was explained to him, in somewhat noble fashion by Dennis Jensen, that money was hardly a consideration compared with the importance to science of establishing the creature's existence. And besides, he pointed out, getting hold of a Sasquatch was a much more involved problem than Metlow seemed to appreciate.

"But I've got one," Metlow said, "and it's sold."

Nobility and scientific priorities fled. "We'll top your best offer," Jensen countered. At this point Fardell and St. Hilaire were somewhere in the wings. The first act was Jensen's alone.

Metlow's story was that on January 27, while out running claim lines (at a location he wouldn't name for the moment), he had come up behind a cream-coloured Sasquatch at a distance of about eighty yards. He said he could make out only its back and that it appeared to be digging ferns out of knee-deep snow and eating the roots. Metlow noted that the surrounding area was well trampled, and he felt the creature was making its home close by. He had brought Streeter along to confirm the story. Streeter was able to confirm that that was the story Metlow had told *him;* after that he faded–in a most judicious move–from the picture.

Throughout the discussion that followed, Metlow, displaying all the time an astonishing facility for avoiding specifics, somehow gave the impression to Jensen that not only did he know where the creature lived, but that he had immobilized it in an abandoned mine shaft. He said nothing more about how much he had been offered, or by whom. Jensen was sold. He stressed to Metlow that the only source of any money worth considering among the Sasquatch hunters was at Northwest Research Association (another name for Roger Patterson) in Yakima, and that he would contact his principals immediately. He did, and Patterson directed him to keep the talking going, and to keep the Dahinden crowd out of it. Schism.

Metlow left, promising to keep in touch.

Roy Fardell and Roger St. Hilaire, the Dahinden camp, knew something was popping. They managed to scrape together the bones of the story and, following some intricate detective work, came up with Metlow. After that it wasn't too difficult to discover the approximate area where Metlow had been prospecting on the day in question. It was somewhere on Frisco Standard, a mountain a few miles to the north.

While these deductions were being pursued, Roger Patterson was in touch with his backer Tom Page, a wealthy Ohio businessman who paid the former rodeo rider an annual retainer to be kept informed of every break in the Sasquatch search. Page flew out immediately, and he and Patterson met and huddled with Metlow, following which

154

the Patterson camp moved its operation to a motel in Colville, twenty-two miles away. The divorce was final.

René reflects on the split somewhat ruefully, and certainly naively: "I thought it had been all for one and one for all before this, but that's not the way it worked out."

The Dahinden camp, its leader in Calgary but in daily contact by telephone, stayed put in Ivan Marx's back yard. Dahinden's orders to the others were to stall, and bluff; to find out what Patterson and Page were offering, and top it. René talked to Metlow by phone but was quite unable to determine whether the man had what he said he had. By now Page was tossing around the figure of thirty-five thousand dollars for a Sasquatch, dead or alive. Metlow remained coy. Page had hired a helicopter from Spokane and had it on constant alert at Colville airport, ready for immediate take-off on Exercise Sasquatch-Retrieval.

The Dahinden company was ready to move whenever the Patterson lot stirred. And there were others. A young newspaperman, Denny Striker of the Colville *Statesman Examiner,* who had been keeping journalistic track of the hunters' presence since the first sighting of the crippled print, could almost taste a massive scoop. If anyone from either camp moved, somehow Striker was after him. He had a jeep sitting in the bush, gassed up and ready to run at the first sign of action. At one point he kept the Patterson motel under observation for seventy-two hours straight, following a tip that the big move was imminent. And the ubiquitous Norm Davis was on the fringe of the action, tagging along with the Dahinden group. Sides were being taken by the usually non-partisan; the border patrol officers committed (unofficially) their help to the Dahinden side, their sense of fair play apparently offended by the selfish attitude suddenly displayed by the Patterson troupe. Ivan Marx stayed neutral, warning Dahinden's men: "If you tell me anything, and the other guys ask me, I'll tell them, so better not tell me anything." As friction grew between the two sides the townspeople grew disenchanted with their one-time favourites. Where once they had stopped to pass the time of day with the adventurers who were keeping the Bossburg-Colville area on the newsmap, now they snubbed them and wished them and their double-dealing long gone.

The hunters' predicament was perhaps best summarized by the one who said: "You couldn't step behind a tree to take a leak without feeling a dozen pairs of eyes on you." The opposing camps followed each other snorting across the hills on snowmobiles, criss-crossing Frisco Standard and the surrounding region. On one occasion, Davis, outfitted in a startling red snowsuit several sizes too big for him, constantly had trouble keeping his seat. Periodically he would roll off as the machine bounced off a ridge or hump and would flounder around up to his buttocks ("like a flaming great snow bunny," as one participant later recalled), a thrashing red figure against the gleaming snow, while his companions plaintively called, "Hurry, Dickie, we're going to lose them!"

Metlow was still being coy about his Sasquatch. Finally Page offered him a thousand dollars to confirm the area where he supposedly had the creature. Although no money changed hands, Metlow conceded that it was on Frisco Standard, but he declined to accompany the hunters to the spot. By this time all concerned should probably have concluded that there was nothing to the prospector's story; but they were in the advanced stages of Sasquatch fever, blind to all reason. In a "top secret" move Patterson and Page and group whipped off in their chopper, set down on the top of Frisco Standard, and took to snow shoes. The Dahinden squad was not outdone; a local sympathiser with their cause had provided a light plane, for the price of the cost of fuel. The moment that Patterson and Page left their machine, the "enemy" small plane came buzzing round the mountain, playfully waggling its wings at them as they flapped about in the deep powder snow. It was now that the border patrol man was moved to make his prediction: "I could see the end of it–a shootout on Frisco Standard; one dead Sasquatch and a dozen dead hunters." And indeed one of the more bloody-minded of the Dahinden squad vowed that should the Patterson-Page chopper be sighted homeward bound with a Sasquatch strapped to the skids, it would be blasted from the Bossburg skies.

Metlow was still accepting no offers, but still was making noises that kept the bidding healthy. Dahinden's men were phoning René at 2 a.m. with daily reports. The bids crept up: $35,000, $40,000, $50,000. "Top them," Dahinden ordered. At the same time he phoned John Green, asking him to get down to Bossburg to watch over their interests. Green went, but (according to Jensen), apparently overcome by the same motives that were fuelling the whole fiasco, spent most of his time galloping between the two camps, seeing where the best deal lay for himself. From this came the rift that more or less broke the one-time close Dahinden-Green partnership.

René's final bid, made as he recalls, "from a motel in Calgary where I was without a pot to piss in," was for $55,000. It was enough to call Metlow's bluff. The prospector walked away from the affair, still uncommitted as to the truthfulness or otherwise of his story. Whether René could have raised the $55,000 remains academic–but chances are that he couldn't.

Metlow wasn't finished with the hunters yet though. When the Frisco Standard smoke had cleared, René, by now back in Bossburg and in an apparent moment of truce with the Patterson team, paid a visit with Jensen to Metlow's home. Conversation was general and quite genial until Metlow casually mentioned that he had a Sasquatch foot in his freezer. The fur hit the fan again. René immediately offered five hundred dollars for one peek at the exhibit. Metlow raised him to five thousand dollars. The excitement brought Dickie Davis to the scene, antennae quivering. Before you could say, "Bigfoot," Davis had a contract sketched out. It would include John Green to write the book, Bob Titmus to skin and dissect the foot's owner–

presumably stashed in a cave somewhere above the snow line–and anthropologist Grover Krantz (for his evaluation of the Sasquatch see Chapt. 9) to introduce it to science. René was out, so was Patterson.

René was still trying to assess Metlow. Did he or did he not have something? He spun a fine yarn, but it was very, very flexible. Now Metlow modified his foot story; the thing wasn't actually in *his* freezer, it was in a freezer at his sister's home near Portland, where he had sent it for safekeeping. They would have to go there to retrieve it. Right, said Davis, and sprung for two return air tickets. By now money was running at flood volume between Davis and those he had named to the contract; but it was all on paper and destined to stay there, except for what Davis lost in his flush of enthusiasm to make more.

Davis and Metlow set out for Spokane from where they would emplane for Portland. Only one of them made it. On the way to the plane from the Spokane terminal building Metlow slipped on some ice and injured his ankle. He had to have it treated, he judged, before going anywhere. "You go on to Portland, Dickie," he said, "I'll get this fixed and then I'll get the next flight out." Like a lamb Davis followed the instructions and flew off to Portland, where he waited two days. He could have waited much longer. Metlow, not the wasteful sort apparently, had cashed in his plane ticket, bought a couple of bottles of the best tasting pain-killer and retired to his home to rest the injury. Davis phoned frantically and in vain from Portland, then returned. "I was real sick, Dickie, I couldn't make it," Metlow explained.

The Metlow chase was exhausted. While the prospector never did concede that he was operating a hoax–or worse–it was obvious to the Sasquatch squads that they'd been had. Several of the police officers in the area, who had followed the developments with a mixture of amusement and incredulity, suggested seriously to René that the prospector should be invited into the bush and persuaded to clear the whole thing up. They swore they would look determinedly the other way. But René settled for warning Metlow, in somewhat dramatic fashion and to the prospector's expressed concern, that wherever he went from then on he would be under surveillance by a considerable network of electronic bugging devices. Metlow faded gracefully from the scene. Davis attempted to save some face by accusing René of souring the deal by offering $55,000 that he obviously didn't have. "But that was for a Sasquatch that Metlow didn't have either," René rationalized.

The episode had cost everyone money and had made all of them appear gullible, though some more than others. René says of it: "It's a pity it happened; it was stupid and it gave the business a bad name. But then in a way I'm not sorry it happened. It taught me a lot about the people I had been working with." The Sasquatch hunters packed their gear and cleared out of the Bossburg region.

The Metlow intrusion, while it demonstrated perhaps one good reason why scientists generally tended to steer clear of the Sasquatch business, did not in any way help to answer or clarify the issue of the crippled prints that had brought René and the others to Bossburg in the first place. It served only to take attention away from them. And the mystery wasn't helped any by what happened next in the continuing Bossburg saga. And here we consider the film mentioned earlier in this chapter.

Back in Vancouver René kept his finger on the Bossburg pulse through regular telephone contact with Ivan Marx. And it seemed that every time he called, Marx had found something; a handprint here, a footprint there, signs of an unusually heavy creature bedding down in the bush; always something to keep the trail warm.

Marx phoned him one evening that October (1970) and said, "I've got a film of the cripple."

The hows and wherefores of the filming were reported in the Colville *Statesman Examiner* under the byline of Denny Striker, late of the Metlow pursuit:

On the night of Oct. 6 an unidentified person

159

called the Marx home, leaving a vague message that either a car or a train had struck a large upright creature on the highway about seven miles north of Bossburg. Marx was away at the time but when he received the message ... he left immediately for the area with a hunting dog he hoped would follow the spoor of the Sasquatch, if indeed that was what it actually was.

Marx was armed with nothing more than a Bolex 16mm movie camera with a 17mm lense, a 35 mm Nikon and a two-way radio with which he had contact with rancher Don Byington, who was in the area by the time Marx's dog had located the creature.

The day was heavily overcast with smoke ... when Marx jumped the creature in the bottom of a dense draw and began filming. The initial footage shows a large black upright figure moving stealthily but rapidly through the dense growth, but only in silhouette.

Marx pressed the pursuit with his hound, forcing the Sasquatch into a clearing where, with his movie camera set at f 2.8 he took the remarkably clear footage of an impressive looking creature.

On the screen the Sasquatch is shown moving from right to left at an angle of about forty-five degrees away from the photographer. Distance from the subject according to Marx ranged from twenty-five feet to more than a hundred feet as it made its way into the heavy underbrush on the far side of the clearing.

Probably the most impressive part of the film, besides its extreme clarity, is the fact that the Sasquatch is visibly injured, holding its right arm tightly to its chest and using its long muscular left arm for compensating balance.

Also, both ankles of the creature seem badly skinned, the wounds showing plainly raw against the black hair of the legs and feet.

In watching the frames singly, the injured or

skinned area appears to extend onto the bottom of one foot, and possibly on both feet, which would account for the apparent pain-filled movements of the frightened creature.

As the Sasquatch is nearing the far side of the clearing, a twisted tree limb is stepped on, bouncing up and striking it above knee level. Marx, the following day, photographed this stick which was ten feet long. In comparison the creature photographed would have stood about nine feet tall and Marx estimated its weight as that of two large bears, or around seven to eight hundred pounds.

The only thing the film is lacking is facial features on the creature. Twice while crossing the clearing the Sasquatch turned its head to glare at Marx. The first time it turned 180 degrees and uttered a weird scream which was heard by Byington, positioned on a ridge nearby. The second time it turned a full 360 degrees, appearing quite confused, but the lack of light prevented any facial features from showing plainly....

Marx said he continued pursuit of the creature until darkness prevented further advance, and when the trail was recovered the following day, it led through a maze of rugged terrain and finally to a body of water where it was lost. He feels the Sasquatch is very old and apparently hurt quite badly....

Striker finished the story with a statement from René who had arrived in Bossburg: "Ivan has a movie and that leaves only two choices. Either it is real or it is not. That's what I'm here to find out."

The story had been released to the wire services and the second seige of Bossburg was under way. Dickie Davis was right back in the fray, tossing offers around for the film, author Ivan Sanderson phoned on behalf of *Argosy* Magazine, and the usual crowd of Sasquatch devotees was there.

Tom Page flew in dangling before Marx a cheque for $25,-000, for the film or a copy of it. He made the proposition–possibly out of desperation, in light of his earlier experiences at Bossburg–that Marx could have the cheque if he would confirm *or deny* the authenticity of the film. Whether he would have honoured the offer if Marx had said the film was faked is a moot but nonetheless intriguing question. The fact that Marx declined that offer should have loaned immediately to the film at least a touch of uncertainty.

Most of the hunters were saying for publication that Marx had the genuine article. René conceded reluctantly that such might be the case, more from a desire to believe Marx's wife, whom he respected and liked and who was confirming her husband's story, than from conviction. John Green arrived and wasted no time in declaring the film authentic. He offered Marx eight hundred dollars for a copy, of which action René reflects dryly, "I guess he wanted two Sasquatch films." (The other one being the Patterson film.) Green was moved to write a tribute to Marx for the pages of the *Bigfoot Bulletin,* a mimeographed publication sent out intermittently from a base in Oakland, California. Part of it read: "I am satisfied...that he could not have faked all he has to show, and that the film is genuine."

Don Byington, the rancher who had been within walkie-talkie distance of Marx when the film was shot, had two young children, and these youngsters, from the time the film was first shown, were heard to murmur that they knew well the location of the filming (Marx had kept the spot secret). No one paid them any heed. The film stayed in limbo and the winter marched on. Still Marx had taken no offer for his film, had released no part of it for publication in any medium.

Then on the scene came Peter Byrne, a British adventurer and hunter who had been part of the Tom Slick-sponsored expeditions in the Himalayas and in northern California. Byrne still had a source of financing and he and

162

Marx came to an arrangement: Marx would be paid a monthly retainer as a Sasquatch hunter of $750, and his film would be placed in a bank safety-deposit box as security. This arrangement carried through to the spring of 1971, Marx being comfortably subsidized to pursue his hunting while at the same time having to make no commitments about the film. But Peter Byrne was considerably less gullible than might have seemed. The Byington children kept harping, as kids will, about how they knew exactly where the film had been shot, and Byrne listened to them. The children led the hunters to a spot at the back of the Byington property immediately recognizable as the film site.

In the film the creature brushes its head against a tree limb. The limb was located and was found to be less than six feet from the ground, shaking Marx's estimate of nine feet for the creature's height. And a comparative film indicated that certain features on the Marx film could not have appeared as they did if he had filmed from the spot he said he had filmed from and with the equipment he said he had used. It was then established, through Peter Byrne's persistent probing, that Marx's camera on the day of the filming was equipped with a telephoto lense and not, as he had said, a regular one. And finally it was discovered that shortly before the film was taken Marx had been buying a considerable quantity of fur pieces in Spokane. The case fell apart, Marx by this time having left the area. The unkindest cut came for Peter Byrne when he went to the bank to inspect his security and found only a roll of black, exposed celluloid.

Later Marx claimed to the others that he had taken and passed a lie detector test over the incident and had passed it, but no one ever knew where or when this had occurred. René's response to the claim is a cryptic: "I'm sure he could take one any time and pass it with flying colours."

(There was a sequel to Marx's fling at cinematography in the fall of 1972. On Saturday Oct. 21 he appeared on *You*

163

Asked For It, a U.S. television show that pursues odd and interesting items at the request of its entranced audience. This time Marx was both the requestee and one of the subjects. He appeared with the show's host, clutching a sealed can of movie film of a creature he said he had photographed during a snow storm in northern California. Marx's never-ending search for the truth had once more culminated in his seeing a Sasquatch, this time a white one. He had followed it through the deepening snow until he realized he could predict its route and, as he quaintly put it, "head it off at the pass." This he did, having enough time to set up his camera, tripod and all, before the thing lurched into view. The TV host then explained that Marx had brought the film straight from the camera, unprocessed, and that the show's producer would print the film under the strictest of supervision and would then examine it. Following a commercial break we were flashed ahead in time to where the film had been processed, and we saw the subject. It was marvellously clear, and outrageous. A primate expert whom the TV people had co-opted for an opinion said it best: "I think it's a man in a beast's suit." It certainly was *someone* in a beast's suit. Great folds of the suit swung around like an old army blanket amid the California snows as the thing cavorted before the camera, now running comically towards it, now turning about and gallivanting off through the drifts, flipping its clumsy feet backwards and sideways as one does when running through deep snow in an overcoat. It seemed almost to be chuckling as it went. Whether Marx was the perpetrator or the victim of a hoax in this case will likely remain unanswered. But there was little doubt that what we were watching was a snowjob in a blizzard.)

So the crippled footprints of 1969 had set in motion a chain of events that went full circle and arrived at nothing, while the prints themselves were, for the time being, virtually forgotten. The events had undoubtedly placed under a cloud the search for the Sasquatch and those few who, like

René, remained seriously and honestly devoted to it. And while the Bossburg exercises provide apparently more entertainment than anything else, they are anything but irrelevant in the Sasquatch saga. For René especially they were enlightening. He saw what he had regarded for the most part as trust between a few people with a unique interest disintegrate into suspicion, deceit, and raw opportunism when the chips were down. René is an honest man and the display disgusted him. But more than that, and more important to him, if he had not been convinced before, he certainly knew now that among his colleagues gullibility increased in direct proportion to any incentive that held the shape of a dollar.

René said a great deal about his colleagues–probably without realizing it–when he told the intrepid Denny Striker at the end of one interview: "We're an exclusive group us Sasquatch hunters, largely because no one wants to join us."

Now, with the histrionics concluded, we can return to the crippled footprint, and, for the argument *for* its authenticity, to Napier. In Chapter 5 of *Bigfoot*, Napier, after a complex explanation of foot anatomy which need not be fully pursued here, concludes that there are two kinds of Sasquatch prints, which he catalogues as the "hourglass" and the "human" types.

The "hourglass," so named because of its shape, is of the kind found at Bluff Creek, the "human" is the Bossburg print. While Napier stresses that the differences between the two walking patterns would, if both types are assumed to be genuine, indicate two species of Sasquatch, and concludes that such a possibility is beyond reason, he still is able to make a case for the validity of both. This of course presents a radical contradiction; but that is nothing new in the Sasquatch story and must wait for an answer until the whole issue is finally resolved. After explaining that the "hourglass" prints provide a strong case for acceptance because of their "persuasive consistency" and their "variability" (in that the variety of anatomical detail they display, as opposed to the uniformity one would expect from a fake, is perfectly in tune with nature) Napier says:

> Apart from satisfying the criteria established for modern human-type walking, the Bossburg prints have, to my way of thinking, an even greater claim to authenticity. The right foot of the Bossburg Sasquatch is a club-foot, a not uncommon abnormality.... The forepart of the foot is twisted inwards, the third toe has been squeezed out of normal alignment, and possibly there has been a dislocation of the bones on the outer border (but this last feature may be due to an imperfection in the casting technique). Club-foot usually occurs as a congenital abnormality, but it may also develop as the result of severe injury, or of damage to the nerves controlling the muscle of the foot. To me the deformity strongly suggests that injury during life was responsible. A true, untreated, congenital (club-foot) usually results in a fixed flexion deformity of the ankle in which case only the forepart of the foot and toes touch the ground in normal standing. In these circumstances the heel impression would be absent or poorly defined; but in fact the heel indentation of the Sasquatch is strongly defined. I conclude that the deformity was the result of a crushing injury to the foot during early childhood.
>
> It is very difficult to conceive of a hoaxer so subtle, so knowledgeable–and so sick–who would deliberately fake a footprint of this nature. I suppose it is possible, but it is so unlikely that I am prepared to discount it.

And there we can leave Bossburg and the cripple for now. Dr. Napier's general Sasquatch thesis will be examined further in Chapter 9, alongside views of other authorities, some of whom lend his conclusions support and others who are determinedly on the opposite side of the Sasquatch fence.

166

CHAPTER 9

According to Prof. John Napier there is a simple formula for the Sasquatch dilemma:

"Either some of the footprints are real, or all are fakes. If they are all fakes, then an explanation invoking legend and folk memory is adequate to explain the mystery. But if any of them is real then as scientists we have a lot to explain. Among other things we shall have to rewrite the story of human evolution. We shall have to accept that Homo Sapiens is not the one and only living product of the hominid line, and we shall have to admit that there are still major mysteries to be solved in a world we thought we knew so well."

While it is encouraging that Napier concedes the possible need to rewrite established theories, his formula is very much an oversimplification, especially where the question of faked footprints is concerned. No matter how many legends and folk memories are invoked, the question would still remain of how the prints were faked. And Napier himself of course stresses the virtual impossibility of someone being equipped to construct a fake such as that of the Bossburg cripple.

His "either-or" theme is echoed in various ways by most of those scientists who have kept an open mind on the mystery, such as the previously-mentioned Prof. Grover Krantz of the anthropology department at Washington State University. In a letter to me in September 1972, Krantz wrote:

> Small anatomical items can be seen in many of these tracks which correspond to logical expectations for the foot of a giant hominid. Either of two conclu-

sions must follow: 1. Sasquatch is real, and that is ridiculous, or 2. a brilliant anatomist designed the fakes which have been placed by a secret organization, and I regard that as impossible. Thus the ridiculous alternative would appear to be true.

This pungent and effective reasoning was extended in the conclusions to one of Krantz's papers (Northwest Anthropological Research Notes, Vol. 6, No. 1, 1972) titled "Anatomy of The Sasquatch Foot," which he generously provided for use in this book. (The preliminary and larger part of the paper we'll get to in a moment.) In his conclusions, Krantz wrote:

> There are a number of reasons to believe at least certain Sasquatch tracks could not have been made by hoaxers. Their obscure locations would mean that perhaps a hundred times as many tracks were laid as have been discovered. Lengths of stride and obstacles stepped over often surpass anything a man can do. Depths of imprints would require a hoaxer to carry many hundreds of pounds of extra weight, thus making the walking accomplishments even more impossible. Independent toe movements as noticed in some tracks would require a special device to accomplish.
>
> To all these must be added the fact that our supposed hoaxer is an expert on human anatomy with a very inventive mind. He was able to create from nothing all the details of how a foot might be redesigned to support a body weight several times that of a man. And he has continued to plant these tracks over more than a lifetime, always showing only vague hints of these anatomical peculiarities....
>
> No matter how incredible it may seem that the Sasquatch exists and has remained uncaught, it is even more incredible to believe in all the attributes of the hypothetical human track-maker. As Sherlock Holmes put it, "...when you have eliminated the impossible,

whatever remains, *however improbable,* must be the truth." Even if none of the hundreds of sightings had ever occurred, we would still be forced to conclude that a giant bipedal primate does indeed inhabit the forests of the Pacific Northwest.

Prof. Krantz's conclusion is drawn from his analysis of the foot after studying casts of seventeen different prints and photos of another fifty casts and prints. His reasoning as we shall see assumes an extra and quite dramatic significance in the light of theories developed by Dmitri Bayanov and Igor Bourtsev, two Moscow colleagues of the late Prof. Boris Porshnev. These theories have not been published before, at least in the western world.

First though to the essence of Krantz's argument for the design of the Sasquatch foot.

He stresses that body weight is the "major factor" in understanding the design and adds, having closely studied the range of estimated sizes: "I am inclined to set nine feet and half a ton as the greatest size of bipedal primate that could properly function." (Note that he is not saying that that is the size of a Sasquatch; he is dealing in theoretical extremes.)

He points out that increases in body size require modifications in body design. For instance, if a man's height were doubled, keeping all proportions the same, in relation to the weight he would have to manoeuvre, his strength would be cut in half. Body-design changes, especially lever lengths, would be desirable to keep movement normal. And: "The large size indicated for Sasquatch poses the same kind of problem."

One of the consistent elements of Sasquatch prints is the absence of an arch. They are uniformly flat. It is this flatness that has led many skeptics to dismiss them as obvious fakes. However, according to Krantz, the opposite would seem to be the case:

> In man this arch is maintained by ligaments and by

169

the muscular pull on tendons. Given five hundred pounds or more of body weight, these structures would not have sufficient increased strength, and the arch would have to flatten....

If a number of people were making fake Bigfoot prints, it might be expected that many of them would not have thought about this characteristic and would have included arches comparable to their own. None of the evidence I have examined shows a normal human arch.

Krantz then examines the mechanics of walking, pointing out that the foot can be viewed as a simple lever at the end of the leg. When a step is taken, the calf muscles tighten, then pull up the heel. The foot pivots at the ankle and the front part presses down, thus starting the "step-off" action. The power arm of the lever (the heel) is relatively short and the load arm (forefoot) relatively long. "This is the normal human condition."

Assuming a drastically increased body weight and a less-proportionate increase in muscle strength, the action described becomes "no longer possible in sustained walking." In other words, "if his foot were built just like a man's, the Sasquatch would not have enough strength in his calf muscles to easily lift his vastly greater bulk with each step."

According to all reports of course the Sasquatch is extremely mobile and agile. Which leaves the conclusion that its foot is not built just like a man's.

Krantz says the simplest way to handle the problem–of maintaining mobility with increased weight–is to change the length of the lever arms. "If the heel ... is lengthened, greater force is applied to the step-off; if the forefoot is shortened, less force is required." In other words, the ankle joint must be set relatively further forward on the foot.

This being the case, the heel section would be correspondingly longer: "This is difficult to measure in footprints but in some cases it is clearly evident. (And) rather than being simply longer, the heel region is wider as well—typically one third of the foot length. Such a general enlargement of the (heel bone) should be expected for greater stability and to provide greater breaking strength in proportion to the increased strain put upon it."

Krantz then reasons that the Sasquatch toes, if used to supplement the step-off with a "push-off" (a reasonable conjecture, considering the weight being moved), would need to be more nearly equal in size and strength than is the case with man, and that they would have to be "more nearly squared off instead of being strongly tapered as in man."

And, he says:

> Many Sasquatch footprints show nearly equal-sized toes lined up almost straight across in a rather non-human manner as might be expected.... Curiously there are also several reported Bigfoot prints which do not show much of these traits, but appear rather more human in the toes. There are two possible explanations for this. Sasquatch feet may include a great range of variation from a nearly human set of toes at one extreme to the ideal type described above at the other extreme. The second possibility is that some of these prints were faked, at least in part, by enlarging the impression of the first toe to make them look more "convincing." I would rather not choose between these two alternatives at the present time.

In summary Krantz says:

> In general the Sasquatch foot differs from man's in having greatly enlarged ankle bones, especially the heel, very short (forefoot), and a more nearly equal set of toes.
>
> These characteristics are all logical requirements for an otherwise human foot adapted to a body weight

of five hundred pounds or more. These characteristics are also evident in preserved footprints.

The significance of Krantz's reasoning on the size of the heel bone becomes apparent in no small way as we come to the theories of the Russians Bayanov and Bourtsev. Their analysis was provoked by and deals with the Patterson film, which they studied for almost a year following René's visit to Moscow, before committing their conclusions to paper.

Their covering letter to René indicates their general attitude to the research:

> Dear René:
> Here is one of the first and, we hope, mellow fruits of Soviet-American cooperation in the field of hominology.
> ...It seems we have found a really strong and scientific argument for the authenticity of the film and footprints.
> And this has become possible first of all because of your, let's say, historic (at least, in the short history of this research) visit to Moscow, which brought us the film and other materials, also because of Grover Krantz's very important article ... and, last but not least, because of our own dedication....
> Hence this material which we call preliminary because we still hope to get other specialists' (in biomechanics, for instance) replies to specific questions we asked them....*
> We hope that even this preliminary result deserves the attention of our American friends....

Some of the material in the Russians' report, such as descriptions of the creature on the Patterson film, will be repetitious, but for the sake of presenting the material in-

---

* See Appendix.

tact (if only because it is from Russia and therefore a fresh view), we ask the reader's indulgence. This is their report:

GENERAL REMARKS ON THE FILM–Roger Patterson's filmstrip shows a hairy man-like creature, walking erect, having well developed breasts and buttocks. The last three points, if we accept for a time the authenticity of the creature, indicate its belonging in the Hominid, not the Pongid (apes) line of evolution of higher primates.

Morphology of the head shows a very outstanding brow ridge, a low ridge of the nose, very pronounced prognathism (jutting jaws), a cone-shaped back of the head.

Judging by the well-developed breasts the creature is female. However, the muscles of the back, arms and legs are so much in relief that they call for comparison with those of a heavy weightlifter.

The creature "has no neck," or at least the neck is not to be detected at first sight. Looking back the creature turns its upper torso along with its head to a much greater extent than would normally a human being. This might indicate a somewhat different attachment of the skull to the spine than in man, and a strong development of the neck muscles which conceal a short, sort of simian neck.

In the initial frames where the creature is standing, then walking in a stooped posture, one is struck by the great flexibility of its spine, which is surprising in so bulk a body. This quality may be of an adaptive nature: picking berries, digging roots and rodents' holes the relict hominoid must be a habitual "stooper." One reason for the large size of the creature's thigh muscles as seen in the film may well be the necessity for the hominoid to squat frequently and move in that position while feeding, as attested by some sighting reports.

173

LOCOMOTION AS SEEN IN THE FILM–It seems smooth and resilient like that of a big quadrupedal animal. One gets the impression that the creature steps on slightly bent legs. If that is the case the impact on the heels should be less manifest than in man's walk, and the hominoid tracks, usually rather even in depth, seem to corroborate this conclusion. While walking, the creature swings its arms intensely, using them as walking beams as it were.

COMPARISON TO SUPPOSED GAIT OF NEANDERTHALER –Prof. Boris Porshnev who put forward the Neanderthal hypothesis of the relict hominoid origin ... refers to the opinions of anthropologists V.P. Yakimov, G.A. Bonch-Osmolovsky and V.V. Bounak concerning the walk of Neanderthalers as construed by analysts of fossil material. We find it very significant that the two characteristics mentioned above–i.e. less impact on the heels and arms swinging–are listed by anthropologists as supposed traits of Neanderthal locomotion, while slightly bent legs are ascribed to Neanderthalers even in a standing position.

THE HOMINOID FOOT–The main features standing out both in the American and Soviet material: 1. Tracks show flat feet (without an arch). 2. The width of the foot in proportion to the length is much greater than in man's foot. 3. The hominoid foot is generally much bigger than man's.

Besides, as has been often noted by Pyotr Smolin, chairman of the Hominoid Problem Seminar at the Darwin Museum in Moscow, the hominoid foot is distinguished by a great mobility of its toes which can bend very much or more fully extend or spread very widely....

Grover Krantz finds the correlation between the great weight of the creatures in question ... and the anatomy of the foot, as it is revealed in the ... footprints, so natural and binding that he makes the following conclusion: "Even if none of the hundreds of sightings had ever occurred, we would still be forced to conclude that a giant bipedal primate does indeed inhabit the forests of the Pacific Northwest."

It's the first time such a unambiguous statement has been made by a professional anthropologist regarding the problem of relict hominoids, a statement made even more welcome by the fact that it came about as a result of study of material evidence–the plaster casts and photographs of footprints.

COMPARISON TO THE NEANDERTHAL FOOT–As far as we know, none of the American researchers has compared the hominoid foot, as revealed in footprints, to the Neanderthal foot, reconstructed on the basis of fossil material.

In the Soviet Union this job has been done by Prof. B.F. Porshnev who noted a similarity in such features as lack of an arch, the width to length ratio, (and) great mobility of toes....

It seems that a new and very important development in this direction of research is a comparison made by us between the (heel bone) of the Neanderthal foot and that of North American hominoids as shown in the materials of American hominologists.

As the enclosed photos show (see illustration), the heel bone of Neanderthaler is much bigger than that of man. Grover Krantz, on his part, concludes that the Bigfoot has "enlarged heels...." He also writes that the creature's "ankle joint must be set relatively farther forward along the length of the foot...."

Well, this is also true for the Neanderthal foot, as can be seen at a glance in the enclosed photos which graphically and, shall we say, dramatically illustrate the above points.

To make things even more fascinating, the very same features show on the foot of the creature in Roger Patterson's filmstrip.... To our knowledge, this fact

175

has not been mentioned before by analysts of the film.

They're right of course, the fact had not been mentioned. What was mentioned though was the man in the Canadian National Museum in Ottawa who rejected the film because he saw a "human heel" protruding from the skin. If the Russians are correct, one can only wonder what this says for our man in Ottawa.

It follows that in analysing a possible anatomy of the hominoid foot we find agreement in three, apparently, independent sources: 1. Roger Patterson's film; 2. Photographs and plaster casts of footprints obtained by René Dahinden and others, and analysed by Grover Krantz; 3. Morphology of the Neanderthal foot.

NEANDERTHAL OR PITHECANTHROPUS?–This (the above conclusions) on the one hand says a lot for the authenticity of the film and footprints, and, on the other, gives more weight and substance to the Porshnev theory....

Yet there is, in our opinion, one serious obstacle to identifying the Patterson film creature with a relict of the Neanderthal stage of evolution, which is that the creature's head is much too ape-like. An ape-like head on a man-like body is rather the formula for Pithecanthropus as follows from anthropological studies of fossil materials.

Napier also commented on the apparent contradiction of the ape-like head in the Patterson film. However he left the question open, if not suspect, whereas the Russians, as we shall see immediately, offer a possible explanation. It should also be remembered here that the whole history of ancient man has depended entirely on the study of relatively few fossil remains and is accordingly incomplete and often highly speculative, and that paleontologists are in frequent disagreement on both chronology and relationships of fossils.

Bayanov and Bourtsev continue:

It was the opinion of the late Prof. Alexander Mashkovtsev that relict hominoids are survivors of the Pithecanthropus stage of evolution of bipedal primates. Unfortunately, for lack of fossil material the Pithecanthropus foot has not yet been reconstructed, but it can be expected that the features of the Neanderthal foot ... were more or less present in the Pithecanthropus foot as well.

Still, the worth of the Porshnev theory, as we understand it, is not in its offering a clue to exact classification of relict hominoids, which it doesn't, but in shedding new light on and, in fact, revolutionizing the entire approach to the problem of evolution of bipedal primates.

According to that theory such terms as Neanderthal Man or Java Man (Pithecanthropus) are a misnomer. The creatures were not men but animals, since man begins where speech begins, and both their morphology and artifacts tend to show that Pithecanthropus and Neanderthalers (with maybe just a few exceptions in the latter) had no speech, no abstract thinking.

If that is so, we can expect that in certain areas of the earth there remains relict "Neanderthal beasts," in other areas–"Pithecanthropus beasts," still in a third–mixed forms of the former two or even other forms. For the evolution of the family Hominidae ... proceeded at such a fast pace (in terms of evolution) that the forms it created were, so to speak, on the move and genetically open, not set and sealed like species created in a very long and slow evolutionary process....

NOT MAN-MADE–So our conclusion at this stage is the following: though it is not yet clear in what relation North American hominoids stand to the making of man, it is pretty clear now that they themselves are not man-made."

Bayanov and Bourtsev conclude the analysis with a comment about the controversial heel evident in a frame of the Patterson film. The comment, as well as providing a neat synthesis of the Russian/Krantz theory, may be read as a further assessment of the judgment of our unnamed man in Ottawa:

"The creature's foot, seen in this picture, has an unnaturally protruding heel. To a casual observer this may seem a sticking-out edge of an artificial sole, but to those who know better this is an omen of the creature's reality."

The two Russians have played an important part in René's approach to the problem ever since their introduction in Moscow and, in a letter dated December 9, 1972, Bayanov took René to task for persisting in holding reservations about both the Patterson film and the Sasquatch dilemma generally. He said:

"...I want to ask you why you 'are still not happy with the explanation' and why the film is still 'driving you crazy.' I'd expect that now, on the contrary, it would be driving you sane.... Don't you see with your own eyes in the photo that the Neanderthal heel bone is bigger than in man?

"As for me, I *felt* the film was true the first time I saw it, whereas now I *know* it is true and I'm satisfied. Which does not mean I will refuse to consider any evidence to the contrary or won't welcome new facts in favour.... Sure, one must be thorough and painstaking in investigation but there should be a reasonable limit to everything, including doubts. By doubting all things all the time one exhausts one's creative strength and does harm to the very investigation in the name of which one has all these doubts."

And as if to supplement his mild lecture on positive thinking, Bayanov included with the letter the following translation of an article from a Soviet Youth magazine, *Tekhnika Molodyozhi* (Technology for Youth), and his comments about it.

The article was titled "I've seen an Almasti" and it read:

178

In December 1941, V.S. Karapetian, a Lt.-Col. in the Army Medical Corps, happened to observe a strange hairy man in the Caucasus. Our correspondent asked Vazgen Sergeyevich Karapetian to tell our readers about that incident and his attitude to it....

"The man I saw," said the army doctor, "is quite clear in my memory as if standing in front of me now. I was inspecting him on the request of local authorities. It was necessary to establish whether the strange man was an enemy saboteur in disguise. But it was a totally wild creature, almost fully covered with dark brown hair resembling a bear's fur, without a moustache or beard, with just slight hairiness on the face. The man was standing very upright, his arms hanging down. He was higher than medium, about 180 centimetres. He was standing like an athlete, his powerful chest put forward. His eyes had an empty, purely animal expression. He did not accept any food or drink. He said nothing and made only inarticulate sounds. I extended my hand to him and even said, 'Hello.' But he did not respond. After inspection I returned to my unit and never received any further information about the fate of the strange creature."

The magazine artist reconstructed the appearance of the Almasti with the help of the army doctor.

Bayanov said of the story:

"Karapetian himself never used the word 'almasti.' In fact this name is used by local inhabitants in another part of the Caucasus. In the part where Karapetian saw the creature one of the local names is 'kaptar,' but Karapetian did not use that either. He used such words as 'man, creature, type.'

"I heard Karapetian's story many times as told by him and here's what should be added in summation. Karapetian stressed the fact that the whole thing happened during the war, in fact at a critical moment of it, which explains, number one, why the authorities got interested in the creature, captured and investigated it (suspicion of an enemy ploy), and number two, why there was no follow up and the clue to the case was lost: nobody at that time gave a thought to the potential scientific value of such freaks of nature.

"Looking back, Karapetian mused that besides beastly hairiness the captured subject differed from humans ... in three respects. Firstly, he was cold-resistant, in fact he preferred cold to the warmth of normal room temperatures. The creature was shown to Karapetian in a cold shed and when he asked why it was kept in such cold the answer was: because he sweats very much in the room. Secondly, the subject's eyes and face had a very non-human, animal-like expression. Thirdly, the army doctors noticed that the creature had lice of much bigger size and of different kind than found on humans.

"As a result of the medical check-up, Karapetian gave the authorities his conclusion to the effect that it was not a man in disguise but a really 'very, very wild' subject with all that hair of its own.

"In 1958, when the USSR Academy of Sciences set up a commission to investigate the problem of the snowman, Karapetian was one of the first to supply information, which took the commission by surprise since nobody at that time could accept the possibility of such creatures in the Caucasus (the idea was just as crazy as snowmen in California).

"...following Karapetian's report, and as a result, the Caucasus, of all places, became the main site of our field work."

The Russian material merits consideration for at least three reasons: 1. The remarkable similarities evident in descriptions of the Almas and the Sasquatch, 2. The realization of how much more sophisticated is the attitude of the Russians to their phenomenon, and 3. The encouragement that the Soviet researchers have provided (and are providing) for their Canadian and U.S. counterparts.

180

The first of these reasons provokes an obvious question: could there be any connection between the two creatures?

It's generally accepted that from time to time in the past one million years some kind of land or ice bridge has connected the Asian and North American land masses, in the area of the Bering Strait. And it's accepted that the North American native, along with several animal species (the brown bear and the moose, for example), made his way by this route from Asia. Simple logic would dictate that where one branch of the hominid line made its way, another also could travel. The probability of a direct connection between the two is apparent.

That being the case, we can sum up the major arguments for and against the possibility of it having sustained itself in North America to the present day.

First, could creatures of this size find the food they would require to nourish such a body mass? We touched briefly on the question in an earlier chapter, but it requires further consideration.

One of those scientists who assessed the situation following the first showings of the Patterson film in Vancouver was a well-known B.C. naturalist, David Hancock, a graduate in zoology from the University of British Columbia, and an admitted skeptic of the Sasquatch story. In an article for *Weekend* magazine he wrote:

> But how could such an animal feed, particularly in winter? It is unlikely that even the most experienced human outdoorsman could eke out an existence without tools. Yet, we are not certain our hypothetical animal does not have tools.
>
> The most obvious source of food in the forest is the cambium layer of fir and hemlock trees. Beaver, deer, and porcupine–all lesser animals–use it for winter sustenance. Native Indians chewed it, sucked it, and stewed it.
>
> But it is more likely our animal would be omnivor-

ous–that is, he would eat anything. Certainly the whatever-it-is on the Patterson film has a small stomach, not the characteristic pot-belly of the greens-eating gorilla. Our animal would get protein from deer, mice gleaned from the forest floor and voles from the bogs and alpine meadows. Many Sasquatch stories tell of the animal eating roots and berries.... The rain forest floor is alive with slugs. Could an omnivorous scrounger pass up a shell-less clam? Not likely. In the north, the fall and winter salmon runs would make him just as fat as they make the bears, gulls and ravens....

An animal as large and fast-moving as the one suggested by the Patterson film would require much food to sustain, but supposing it were migratory? The Bluff Creek area...is less than one hundred miles from the sea (in fact it is only twenty miles)–four or five days hike for a long-striding giant. And the Northern California beaches are wild and uninhabited in winter.

Only at night in the winter months are there any really low tides to make clam-hunting and tide-pool scavenging possible. Sleeping in the forest by day, hunting the beaches by night and having the incoming tide wipe out his tracks, old Sasquatch could laugh at the winter. In spring, the succulent young plants, berries and small animals could entice him back to the high country.

Then Hancock tackled the other major question of sustained survival–procreation of a species.

As a skeptic, I would have to say the biggest zoological question on the existence of a Sasquatch is: how is the species perpetuated? How do they breed if there are so few of them spread over such a large area?

Scientifically, as a species decreases, its chances of procreation diminish rapidly to the point where reproduction for the maintenance of the species is impossible and the species dies out....

182

A similar approach to the procreation issue was taken by Phyllis Dolinhow, director of the anthropology department at the University of California in Berkeley, who told the *Wall Street Journal* reporter in August of 1972:

"It's the question of the number of animals necessary to maintain any living species. Taking the fact you need a lot of them, it's very unlikely we wouldn't have found one, especially in an area like the U.S."

As authoritative statements they sound fine—until we point out that Hancock's comment concerning "...so few of them spread over a large area..." unlike his reasoned and documented argument on food supplies, has no foundation. He is simply speculating that there are "so few," and he does not say how many "so few" would be. And Dolinhow's "...it's very unlikely that we wouldn't have found one..." blithely ignores the hundreds of times the creature has been seen in places hundreds of miles apart.

That last fact indeed might give us some indication about the Sasquatch population—taking the position that, "for every one you see there could be X number in existence." To elaborate on that, we can consider a study made in the 1950's by the Michigan Game Commission, who set out to demonstrate the fallacy of complaints from hunters that the deer had all but disappeared.

They built a fence eleven feet high around one square mile of country containing growths of hardwood forests, conifer swamps, and open pine barrens and put thirty-nine deer inside the enclosure. Over a three-year period from three to ten hunters spent eighteen days trying to kill the deer. It soon became obvious to them that though there may be a relatively heavy population concentration, getting close to any of the deer is more of a problem than might first appear.

On a clear, calm day in 1954, six hunters entered the enclosure, where a light snow had made conditions ideal for tracking. The hunters knew how many deer were in the enclosure, and they knew that most of the animals had never been fired at.

It took them four days of hunting even to see a buck and fifty-one hunting hours to take a buck during the buck season. Fourteen hunting hours were needed to take a deer during open season on both sexes.

At all times the hunters were allowed to stalk, trail, stand or organize drives to bring the deer within range.

The lesson is obvious and surely may be applied to any creature living in the wild and constantly aware that to expose itself could mean destruction. And we should remember that in the case of the Sasquatch we are dealing with hundreds of thousands of square miles of territory, much of which sees little of man.

Throughout the book I have quoted Prof. John Napier—because he is the first recognized major authority to present to the general public a definite positive commitment as answer to the mystery. It would be fitting to close this chapter with some of his conclusions.

Napier says that some of the Sasquatch sightings undoubtedly have involved bears, but, he says, "...none of the published footprints ... could conceivably have been made by a bear." And, "...to explain away the sightings and the footprints simply in terms of bears alone is like describing gravity as a phenomenon by which apples are found on the ground."

He says: "No one doubts that some of the footprints are hoaxes and that some eyewitnesses are lying, but if *one* track and *one* report is tru-bill, then myth must be chucked out of the window and reality admitted through the front door...."

And then he puts the Sasquatch case into the simplest and most effective of terms:

"The vision of such creatures stomping barefoot through the forests of north west America, unknown to science, is beyond common sense. Yet reason argues that this is the case."

184

CHAPTER 10

And talking about stomping around, and in keeping with Napier's references to subtle hoaxes–and some not so subtle....

In the soft spring days of May 1977, four young men from a suburb of Vancouver, B.C., decided it was time the public was treated to a Sasquatch sighting. Using information gleaned from an earlier edition of this book, they arranged an event that resulted in the following headline in the local *Columbian* newspaper: "RCMP convinced Sasquatch no hoax."

Now, to convince the Royal Canadian Mounted Police of something unlikely, you have to work at it. When you convince them of the presence of the Sasquatch, you have scaled new heights. The fact that the Mounties in the small city of Mission in the Fraser Valley–and a good many other people –would soon be wearing a considerable amount of egg on their faces, simply attests further to the ingenuity of the four perpetrators.

Here's the scene as played out at about 8:30 a.m. on Sunday, May 15, 1977:

A Pacific Stage Lines bus driven by Pat Lindquist, *en route* to Vancouver from the lake-resort village of Harrison Hot Springs, barrels down Highway 7, about nineteen miles east of Mission. It passes a pickup truck with its hood raised, as if the truck's driver has found a mechanical problem. What the driver really has under the hood is a walkie-talkie radio. As the bus passes, he contacts an accomplice about a mile ahead and advises him that the bus is on the way, just behind a blue van. This accomplice tells his companion standing beside him to get ready. The two young radio men are Rene

Quesnel and Gordon Jacobi from Port Coquitlam, a valley suburb of Vancouver.

A minute later, as the bus, led by the blue van, rounds a bend in the highway, one of its passengers, twenty-six-year-old Don Ticehurst, leaps to his feet, points down the road ahead, and yells something like, "Looka there!"

The bus driver and six passengers see the same thing at the same time. They see Ticehurst's twenty-four-year-old brother, Ken, alerted by his companion with the second radio, burst from the bush and gallop across the highway–dressed in a rented gorilla suit.

But what the driver and passengers think they see, and what RCMP investigators come to firmly believe they saw, was a Sasquatch.

Lindquist jumps on the brakes, leaps from the bus, and chases after the creature as it hurries into the bush.

One of the passengers also leaps from the bus, and starts yelling, but Cathy Byrn's sentient cries are dismissed. She said later: "I ran out of the bus after [the figure] had gone across the road and stood shouting, 'You're not fooling us!'" And her husband said, laconically, "It looked like a man in a black monkey suit or something like that."

Even Lindquist said that, at first, "I thought it was someone trying to con us, so I took off after it."

Then he told reporters his initial anger turned to awe, then to fright, as he gazed at the beast, which he described as being about seven feet tall and weighing 350 pounds, with dark-brown-to-black fur, a light-coloured face with flat, flared nostrils "like a monkey," and large, wide eyes.

He said the first thing he noticed about the creature was the smell–"a horrible smell like very rotten meat," from about a twenty-five-foot distance.

Lindquist described how at no time did the creature make any threatening moves towards him. "It could have taken two steps and grabbed me but it didn't do anything. It didn't growl, it didn't show its teeth. It just looked at me." Maybe, in hindsight, these omissions should have been his first clue. But then there was the smell that Lindquist described, the rotten meat. How to account for that? It is a phenomenon often connected with reports of contact with the mysterious creature. Did Ticehurst perhaps simply step in something as he jogged through the bush? That question was never resolved, indeed it became lost as events unfolded.

The RCMP were quickly on the scene, and right there before their eyes was the evidence that convinced them the sighting was the real thing–thirteen footprints in a hard-sand creek bed. The prints were fourteen inches long and showed the clear imprint of five toes. All the prints differed slightly from each other, as, presumably, would those of someone or something running over uneven ground.

A paragraph in a local paper, the *Progress*, said: "A prankster would be hard put to come up with enough different foot impressions to fool police trackers."

That view was clearly shared by RCMP Const. Robert Eyford, who after a six-hour search of the area, and examining the footprints, stated, "We have found no evidence of a hoax." He added, "I think we've got the best pictures in Canada of Sasquatch footprints."

Radio stations were on to the story like badgers, and, before the day was out, police were directing traffic that brought more than a thousand people to view the evidence. By the end of the day, the footprints were all but obliterated by the shoes of mere mortals.

One of the early arrivals at the scene was René Dahinden, who says simply of the Mission affair, "I was suckered in. You have a bus driver and six passengers who say they saw this thing; you have police who are convinced the thing is real–the whole situation short-circuited my usual suspicions. I did not stand back far enough and examine closely enough what we had."

René had an opportunity to reassess the situation a few days later when Eyford phoned him and said the Mission detachment had received a tip from the Coquitlam RCMP that there might indeed have been some monkey business going on at Mission.

The result was an appearance by the four hoaxers on a radio talk show and a complete admission to and description of their coup. Ticehurst had rented the gorilla suit from a joke and costume shop, had carefully checked bus timetables, and had set up the radio-relay team and the "witness" on the bus.

But most importantly, the gang had prepared for the bus trick by laying down tracks earlier that morning. They had first (using information from this book's earlier edition) made "feet" by carving molds into a clay bank and pouring resin into them. They took the resulting models to the creek bed, set them down, stood on them, and rolled gently back and forth to give the impression of the depth of print that such a heavy creature would make. They used rocks in the creek bed as stepping stones to avoid leaving any prints of their own. "All they had to do then," said Dennis Gates, one of René's colleagues, "was wait for the bus."

The admission drew the inevitable newspaper headlines, the simplest and best of which said: "Four hoaxers admit they aped Bigfoot."

Before the admission, René conducted a lengthy interview with Lindquist in the company of an RCMP staff sergeant. "Certainly Lindquist was not lying," René says. "The guy saw something, close up, and believed it was what he said. So did [most of] those passengers. He was fooled–unless of course there just happened to have *been* a Sasquatch standing there right after the guy in the suit ran off."

The Mounties were said to have been, like the late Queen Victoria, not amused.

The Mission hoax doesn't explain any of the other hundreds of sightings, but it does hold lessons for people like René; lessons about gullibility, and the need for constant skepticism. The chief lesson he learned from Mission was to do with footprints. By the time he got to the site that day, the prints had started crumbling, which gave them a more "natural" look, and it was from the prints in this condition that others made their own molds to be kept as "evidence." When, several days later, René saw police photos of the prints taken early in the morning, right after the sighting, he remarked on how unusually crisp and neat the edges looked, almost as if they could have been made from the same mold....

The Ticehurst admission confirmed his thoughts. From then on he would be more interested in seeing early pictures of supposed footprints, rather than plaster casts. He would be doubly skeptical of future reports of sightings from wide-eyed witnesses.

Five years after the Mission affair, there began what has become a one-man Bigfoot show in Washington State that has put all critical faculties to the test. René still considers it to be a continuing hoax, but with a motive considerably less wholesome than that of the four lads at Mission, who were, after all, just having fun. On the other hand, Grover Krantz, the Washington State University professor of anthropology from whose works we have quoted in earlier chapters, believes that the man at the centre of the Washington State activity, Paul Freeman, has produced some of the best evidence ever that Bigfoot is alive and prowling.

The problem with Freeman's story can be summed up by saying that it seems wherever he goes, Bigfoot, like Mary's little lamb, is sure to follow.

Freeman first came to attention in June 1982, and a more credible source seems hard to find. First newspaper reports said, "In one of the most reliable sightings ever, a government wildlife expert came face to face with a monstrous 450-pound Bigfoot."

Freeman was the so-called expert, although he was just a part-time employee of the state forestry department in Walla Walla, with no professional qualifications. At the time of his first Bigfoot sighting, he said, "I've been working in the wild all my life, and I know a bear or a man in a gorilla suit when I see one–and that's not what I saw. I still can't sleep at night thinking about it."

His description of the creature he saw while patrolling the Walla Walla watershed in his pickup truck was astonishingly detailed–understandably so, as he said he stood and exchanged gazes with it from a distance of only ten feet. It was nine feet tall, weighed about 450 pounds, and was covered with reddish brown hair. It smelled of "a very foul odor, like strong urine."

Freeman was the first to break off the contact as he said he began to feel threatened by the creature's repeated raising of the hair on its neck. Freeman left and reported the event to his superiors, who raised a search party, including tracking dogs. The party saw twenty-one footprints, which disappeared when the ground became rocky. The dogs, Freeman told reporters later, "either couldn't or wouldn't" follow the creature's trail. He also said, "Before all this happened, I was a complete non-believer–but not any more." As we shall certainly see.

The Freeman sighting brought the experts onto the scene as usual, including René and Krantz, and within a short time they had taken completely opposing positions. Krantz was singing Freeman's praises and waving footprint casts as proof–"maybe the best set of prints of a Sasquatch ever obtained." His enthusiasm was based on what he called "dermal ridges" (skin marks) found in the prints. René, who interviewed Krantz, Freeman, and half a dozen others, was declaring the whole thing a crock and Freeman a faker. One of René's chief sources was a legendary U.S. Border Patrol member, Joel Hardin, of whom more in a moment.

René (no doubt with the Mission lesson still firmly in mind), zeroed in on the tracks and declared them fakes. He said that: pine needles had been brushed away from inside the tracks; human prints at the scene sank deeper into the mud than those of the alleged Sasquatch; and neither dogs nor horses brought to the scene almost immediately after the incident showed any reaction to smell.

René advised reporters: "You can fool people but you can't fool animals. I don't have a Ph.D., I just use horse sense when I investigate these things."

René said he was suprised that Krantz had not interviewed Joel Hardin, whose report also concluded the prints were faked. Krantz replied that he had found discrepancies in Hardin's report.

Joel Hardin is a tracking expert in the U.S. Border Patrol and an avid outdoorsman. At the time of the Freeman incident, in an eighteen-year career, he had tracked more than five thousand people and taught hundreds of others how to track. He was asked by the forest service to examine the tracks Freeman found. The reason the forest service gave for asking his assistance was that they were "concerned because entry in the watershed is prohibited except by permit." Whether that was aimed at un-permitted Sasquatches wasn't clear.

In any case, Hardin did not treat any part of the exercise as a joke. His report to the forest service stated in part that the tracks "were a very clever attempt to perpetrate a hoax, [with the thought that] involving your office or agency ...[would] lend authenticity or credibility to [the hoax in the eyes of] the general public."

Giving detailed reasons, he said he believed the tracks were made "using some type of soft plaster or rubber-coated foot." He believed the tracks were made by "someone with normal access to the area, very knowledgeable and interested in 'Bigfoot' legends and stories...."

A report in *Pacific Northwest* magazine the following spring took the Freeman story further. "There were peculiarities to Freeman's story and background," writer Scott Forslund noted. "In 1975 he had made a few tracks of his own–with a pair of 21-inch wooden feet he jig-sawed from a two-by-six plank." And Forslund noted that other Sasquatch hunters were beginning to wonder about Freeman's luck because, six days after his alleged sighting, while patrolling the watershed on horseback with a colleague, Freeman suggested they head for a ridge to eat lunch. Reaching it, he immediately discovered several tracks. He then suggested that perhaps the creek below would be a better picnic site and they moved on down–where they "discovered" eight more tracks.

Freeman left the forest service shortly after this and went to work for a rancher in Oregon. On a fishing trip with the rancher and some friends–men who had hunted and fished the area for decades without finding anything out of the ordinary–Freeman discovered tracks.

René told the magazine writer: "It's awfully suspicious. The first tracks ever discovered in the watershed are discovered by a man who gets the job a month before. Then more tracks are found–not once, but three times–several miles apart. And never unless Paul Freeman is around."

One cannot let the Walla Walla print saga go without including an observation from the Spring 1989 edition of the *Skeptical Inquirer*, the Journal of the Committee for the Scientific Investigation of Claims of the Paranormal. Writer Michael R. Dennett, after quoting Dahinden contemptuously comparing the prints to the notorious fake Hitler Diaries, supports a contention that the tracks could indeed have been made by real, human feet: "The patterns of the [dermal] ridges do not exclude that of a human being with large feet...because several people in Holland have feet nearly of equal length to the [Walla Walla] tracks."

Freeman has made frequent appearances since the watershed tracks. In 1987 he reported finding tracks of four Sasquatches in the Blue Mountains of eastern Washington. In October 1988, he and his son Duane claimed to have taken a photo of one near the watershed tracks site. A newspaper reproduction of the picture showed what could have been anything or anyone. Also in 1988, he was talking of starting a museum where Bigfoot mementos would be sold. In June 1989, he told a reporter he had seen Sasquatch on four different occasions, and said he had hair samples. (Krantz has also said he believes the hair samples to be authentic.) In early 1992, Freeman announced he had captured a Sasquatch on videotape. The newspaper report says, "If Freeman had not 'forgotten' to zoom the lens on his camcorder, the black creature captured on film would have been more than an inch tall and less blurry on his big-screen television." Freeman is quoted as saying, "You have to look at it two or three times until you see it."

"At least," adds René.

The Mission escapade and the Freeman saga are the kind of events that serve, says René, in a breathtaking understatement, to "muddy the waters" for the legitimate hunters of Bigfoot.

But there are also moments and events that lend the hunt at least, if not the creature itself, credibility. Such a moment occurred in May 1978 at the University of British Columbia in Vancouver, where scientists and academics gathered for the first time to discuss seriously all manner of monsters and especially the Sasquatch. This was the same venue where the Patterson film was first viewed by an audience of scientists, none of whom was–or indeed has yet been–willing to declare it faked.

The 1978 conference was organized by Marjorie Halpin, curator of UBC's renowned Museum of Anthropology, and Michael Ames, director of the museum and UBC professor of anthropology. Halpin said at the time, "It's time the academic community came out of the closet and seriously addressed the question of the Sasquatch." The closets emptied from across North America as academics and scientists –in disciplines ranging from psychiatry, sociology, and anthropology to electrical engineering–joined plain old Sasquatch hunters in a presentation of monster myth and mystery.

The tone of the twenty-five or so papers presented was that of serious examination by legitimately curious and qualified people of science. The papers were subsequently compiled in the book *Manlike Monsters on Trial: Early Records and Modern Evidence,* edited by Ames and Halpin, and published by the University of British Columbia Press.

In his epilogue to the collected papers, Ames says:

> Most anthropologists...readily accept the proposition that humanoid monsters are cultural creations. But might they also be creatures of nature, actual living beings? This question was asked over and over again at the conference, and though participants, and representatives of the media reporting the event, took sides, most agreed that no generally acceptable answer was available. And though some expressed cautious interest in footprints and in the Patterson film, most of the participants concurred with Grover Krantz's statement that only an actual specimen would resolve the debate.

And he adds revealingly, "I suspect it would take more than one specimen to satisfy the skeptics–preferably a tribe of them for anthropologists to study at their leisure."

EPILOGUE

René Dahinden's file on the Sasquatch grows each year as reports of sightings and discoveries continue.

At this writing the most recent outstandingly documented incident–after the Dawson Creek oil rig event with which we started the book–occurred in 1988, on the May 24 Victoria Day holiday weekend, in the Crandell Lake campground in Waterton Lakes National Park in the southwest corner of Alberta.

Susan Ray Adams and her husband Scott Stoness were on a camping holiday with another couple, Darwin Gillies and his girlfriend Shannon Senkow. All four are from Calgary. The two women are schoolteachers, the men are engineers.

A hand-written report made by Darwin Gillies and given to the park game warden on the morning of the holiday Monday is the first description of what the four campers watched the previous night.

> At approximately 12:50 a.m. at the Crandell Lake campground we spotted a very unusual animal...
>
> We were sitting at our campfire when we heard some snorting. We assumed it was a deer, but on further observation we decided it was a bear and bolted for the cars. The animal was on its hind legs and we switched on the headlights on one of the vehicles. From the shadows I could see the animal was moving on its hind legs so I called to the other vehicle to turn on their lights.
>
> What we saw then was incredible. This animal was not only on its hind legs, it was standing (like a human).

We watched as it walked through the trees for at least three to four seconds. I immediately thought it was a joke. We're all convinced it was not a bear. We jumped into the same vehicle and followed in the general direction it disappeared.

We came across another vehicle and flashed our lights. These people had also sighted something very strange and were quite scared. This confirmed that we had both seen the same thing.

It is important to note that we are four mature, responsible, professional people. We thought very carefully before coming in to report these incidents at the warden's office. All four of us are convinced that it was not a bear. I am equally convinced it was not a practical joke. If it was it was pretty elaborate and well done.

From our sighting, the best description we can give is as follows:

The animal was approx. 8 ft tall (as measured by the tree it was standing beside in our campsite). The animal was never on all fours. When we switched on the headlights and got a good look, this thing was striding and a big strider at that. It also had long arms which were swinging while it moved through the bush. It wasn't a bear, O.K.!

The statement was signed by Gillies on behalf of the four.

More than a year later, each of the four–reluctantly, as they stressed–gave a detailed interview to Tom Steenburg, a colleague of René Dahinden, who took them back over every step of the incident that night.

Each stressed that the creature stood and walked upright on two legs, like a human, and that at no time did it go down on all fours. Each said that at first glance they thought it was a bear, and then very quickly decided it was anything but a bear.

Some excerpts from the interviews:

Susan Ray Adams (after they had fled to the cars and turned on the headlights):

> The creature walked into the light. It was walking on a ridge about 30 to 35 feet away, the headlights shining right on it. It kind of looked back at us but it didn't break its stride. It was obviously getting out of there, but it wasn't really scared or anything, it was just walking. It was about eight feet tall, it had long arms...it was kind of slender but its legs were really long like they were disproportionate to its body...and that's what we saw...and my husband yelled something like, 'Holy shit that's incredible, it's a Sasquatch.'...

She noted that earlier in the evening she had commented to the others on the disappearance from the campgrounds of the deer that are usually there eating from campers' hands.

"There weren't any deer around all that night," she told the interviewer. "And in the morning when the deer had come back I knew that it was safe and whatever this thing was it had disappeared." She said the decision to report the incident to the game warden was made only "after much debate."

Scott Stoness remarked more than once on the snorting/grunting noise the creature made, and on its apparent lack of concern over their presence. "I would say that this animal was never scared, he was maybe ten to fifteen feet away from us, looking right at us, I would say more startled than anything, like we were coming down the trail right towards it and all it did was snort."

Stoness was asked if they had looked for footprints. "Yes, I did [the next day]...but in that area it was rocky with a little bit of moss on top of it, so you could have had an elephant move through there and not leave footprints that I would have been able to distinguish."

Stoness talked of the response he received from the game warden to whom they reported the incident. "I was kind of reluctant to report it at first because I thought, 'What's going to become of this, probably nothing because people are going to think we are cranks,' but Susan and Shannon finally talked us into going and reporting it. We told [the warden] the story and...I think he only half believed us that it was a Sasquatch, and half believed we had seen a bear."

Darwin Gillies and Shannon Senkow gave similar reports, although with some discrepancies in how long the sighting lasted and from what distance. There was little discrepancy, however, in the general description of the creature and in their conviction of what they had seen.

There was one common, repeated thread in the statements–an initial reluctance to talk because of the possible consequences. They had discussed the business with no one but a few close friends between the time of the handwritten report and the interviews a year later.

The dilemma of whether or not to report what one has seen in such situations was considered at the 1978 University of British Columbia conference by Ron Westrum, sociology professor at Eastern Michigan University, in a paper titled "Reporting Scientific Anomalies." He defines an anomaly as "an event that is not supposed to happen," and discusses the problem faced by those people involved when it does happen. What he says boils down to the fact that first you're probably not going to believe your eyes, and that, if you talk about it, neither is anyone else. "The person who has had an anomaly experience is likely to experience a certain amount of 'cognitive dissonance'; a lack of agreement between his beliefs and his experience. The more impressive the experience, the more difficult this problem is likely to be."

By reporting the experience, Westrum says, "the person exposes himself to ridicule. This may come in the form of condescension or laughter [from] the person or persons to whom the report is made, or it may come in the much more damaging form of satire in the press...."

Westrum also talks of the problems that exist for people with genuine reports to make when there have been previously exposed hoaxes in the same area. Westrum says, "Few people enjoy being laughed at. The person who is willing to report an anomaly when several fraudulent reports have recently been exposed is hardy indeed. Many persons who would be willing to make a detailed report if they could find someone sympathetic to report to are discouraged by initial negative receptions created by this atmosphere. The fraudulent report is thus likely to constrict the reporting process."

This speaks volumes for the conviction and courage of the numerous people named throughout this book who have come forward and reported, with the possibility of ridicule as their only reward.

Among all this, there is the occasional bright moment for the career Sasquatch/Bigfoot investigator such as René Dahinden. In October 1990, the Canada Post Corporation issued a set of stamps on Canada's Legendary Creatures, its first in a series commemorating Canadian folklore. A fairly contented-looking, seemingly well-fed and distinctly humanish, hairy Sasquatch was featured on one of four thirty-nine-cent stamps. The others displayed Ogopogo, the frequently sighted water serpent from B.C.'s Lake Okanagan; the Kraken, accounts of which suggest its ancestor was the giant squid; and the Loup-Garou, French-Canada's version of Europe's werewolf. Information on the creatures went out in a glossy educational newsletter-teaching-aid to schools across Canada.

The Sasquatch has also received due attention from Hollywood, with such movies as "Harry and the Hendersons," which, while being perhaps short on the kind of scrutiny René Dahinden applies to the question, provide great entertainment, and must surely still pose the question: Do you really think there is such a thing...?

And at this writing (summer of 1992), an event noted earlier in this book–the intriguing story of Ishi of the stone-age Yahi tribe, found near Oroville, California–has become a major pay-TV movie, starring Graham Greene.

René Dahinden remains as unbendingly skeptical–and as deeply curious–as he has ever been about the question of whether there is a creature we call Sasquatch or Bigfoot. He remains as critical as ever of many of the people involved in the search. "The search for the Sasquatch is a bit like looking for the Holy Grail," he says, "except that it is performed by very unholy people."

The Patterson film remains, to his mind, the most nagging piece of "evidence." He has spent endless hours at the film site, measuring and examining the area relentlessly under similar daylight and climatic conditions. And he keeps viewing the film.

He wishes he could get a greater variety of science disciplines to examine the film in its most minute detail. His aim is not to convince anyone that the film is genuine, but to determine once and for all whether it was or was not faked. "Still today it could be one of the biggest things ever to find out," he says. He leans towards the film's being genuine: "Because despite everything I've done, I have not been able to break it down to show it was faked. And nor has anybody else."

He says: "I have my doubts all the time about what I'm doing: I've always had them. It's a lonely place to be, on one side of the fence with the rest of the world on the other side. But it's where I have to stay.

"I know I won't be able to convince the world by argument, because it doesn't want to be convinced. I just have to keep on going–and I will do–until one of these creatures is found, dead or alive."

If you have any information about Sasquatch/Bigfoot sightings, please contact:
René Dahinden
7340 Sidaway Road
Richmond, B.C. V6W 1B8
Canada

APPENDIX

Qualitative biomechanical analysis of the walk of the creature in the Patterson film:
Conclusions reached by Dr. Dmitri D. Donskoy, Chief of the Chair of Biomechanics at the USSR Central Institute of Physical Culture in Moscow:

As a result of repeated viewings of the walk of the two-footed creature in the Patterson film and detailed examination of the successive stills from it, one is left with the impression of a fully spontaneous and highly efficient pattern of locomotion shown therein, with all the particular movements combined in an integral whole which presents a smoothly operating and coherent system.

In all the strides the movement of the upper limbs (they can be called arms) and of the lower limbs (legs) are well coordinated. A forward swing of the right arm, for example, is accompanied by that of the left leg, which is called cross-limb coordination and is a must for man and natural for many patterns of locomotion in quadrupeds (in walking and trotting, for instance).

The strides are energetic and big, with the leg swung forward. When man extends the leg that far he walks very fast and thus overcomes by momentum the "breaking effect" of the virtual prop which is provided by the leg put forward. Momentum is proportional to mass and speed, so the more massive the biped the less speed (and vice versa) is needed to overcome the breaking effect of legs in striding.

The arms move in swinging motions which means the muscles are exerted at the beginning of each cycle

201

after which they relax and the movement continues by momentum. The character of arm movements indicates that the arms are massive and the muscles strong.

After each heel strike the creature's leg bends, taking on the full weight of the body, and smooths over the impact of the step acting as a shock-absorber. During this phase certain muscles of the leg are extended and become tense in preparation for the subsequent toe-off.

In normal human walk such considerable knee flexion as exhibited by the film creature is not observed and is practised only in cross-country skiing. This characteristic makes one think that the creature is very heavy and its toe-off is powerful, which contributes to rapid progression.

In the swinging of the leg, considerable flexion is observed in the joints, with different parts of the limb lagging behind each other: the foot's movement is behind the shank's which is behind the hip's. This kind of movement is peculiar to massive limbs with well relaxed muscles. In that case the movements of the limbs look fluid and easy, with no breaks or jerks in the extreme points of each cycle. The creature uses to great advantage the effect of muscle resilience, which is hardly used by modern man in usual conditions of life.

The gait of the creature is confident, the strides are regular, no signs of loss of balance, of wavering or any redundant movements are visible. In the two strides during which the creature makes a turn to the right, in the direction of the camera, the movement is accomplished with the turn of the torso. This reveals alertness and, possibly, a somewhat limited mobility of the head. (True, in critical situations man also turns his whole torso and not just head alone.) During the turn the creature spreads the arms widely to increase stability.

In the toe-off phase the sole of the creature's foot is visible. By human standards it is large for the height of the creature. No longitudinal arch typical of the human foot is in view. The hind part of the foot formed by the heel bone protrudes considerably back. Such proportions and anatomy facilitate the work of the muscles which make standing postures possible and increase the force of propulsion in walking. *Lack of an arch may be caused by the great weight of the creature.*

Above emphasis mine: compare this statement with the findings of anthropologists Grover Krantz and of the two Russians Bayanov and Bourtsev, in Chapter 9. Each of these three sources arrived at the same conclusion totally independently of the others.

The movements are harmonious and repeated uniformly from step to step, which is provided by synergy (combined operation of a whole group of muscles).

Since the creature is man-like and bipedal its walk resembles in principal the gait of modern man. But all its movements indicate that its weight is much greater, its muscles especially much stronger, and the walk swifter than that of man.

Lastly, we can note such a characteristic of the creature's walk, which defies exact description, as expressiveness of movements. In man this quality is manifest in a goal-oriented sporting or labour activity, which leaves the impression of the economy and accuracy of movements. This characteristic can be noted by an experienced observer even if he does not know the specifics of given activity. "What need be done is neatly done" is another way of describing expressiveness of movements, which indicates that the motory system characterized by this quality is well adapted to the task it is called upon to perform. In other words, neat perfection is typical of those movements which through regular use have become habitual and automatic.

On the whole the most important thing is the consistency of all the above-mentioned characteristics. They not only simply occur, but interact in many ways. And all these factors taken together allow us to evaluate the walk of the creature as a natural movement, without any signs of artfulness which would appear in intentional imitations.

At the same time, with all the diversity of human gaits, such a walk as demonstrated by the creature in the film is absolutely non-typical of man.

It is important to remember that Dr. Donskoy is neither a Sasquatch hunter nor an anthropologist. He is an expert in biomechanics, and his analysis of the film is made purely from the principles of that discipline.   DH.

CREDITS

$$\frac{\text{the foot's size}}{16^{in}}$$